The World of a Hedge

THE WORLD OF A
HEDGE

Terry Jennings
B.Sc. Ph.D.

with line drawings by Wilhelmina Mary Guymer

FABER AND FABER
London · Boston

First published in 1978
by Faber and Faber Ltd
3 Queen Square London WC1
Printed in Great Britain by
BAS Printers Limited, Over Wallop, Hampshire
All rights reserved

British Library Cataloguing in Publication Data
Jennings, Terry John
  The world of a hedge.
  1. Hedges—Great Britain—Juvenile literature
  2. Ecology—Great Britain—Juvenile literature
  I. Title
  574.5'264   SB437

ISBN 0-571-11179-3

TO IMELDA

Contents

Illustrations

Acknowledgements

I should particularly like to thank my wife for typing and checking the manuscript and for her active assistance and encouragement in preparing this book. Thanks are also due to Miss I. Devine for her help with the illustrations and for her constructively critical comments on the manuscript. Dr J. P. Barkham of the School of Environmental Sciences, University of East Anglia read the text and made many useful suggestions for improvement.

The photographs were taken by the author.

Foreword

Vast forests once covered most of Britain, so a large part of the animal life of our country must have originally belonged to woodland. As the forest diminished and the hedgerows increased, many woodland creatures moved into them, so that apart from serving as a living fence and adding variety and beauty to the landscape, hedges act as a haven for wild life. The chief haven, in fact, since the total area of hedgerows and their accompanying verges, some 180,000 hectares (450,000 acres), is said to be twice that of the official nature reserves of this country. Of the different groups of animals, nearly half the British species of mammals, butterflies and bumblebees, all the six species of reptiles, and forty of the 200 breeding birds, as well as many other animals, may be regarded as permanent residents of hedges and verges in different parts of the country. In addition, twenty-seven of Britain's 300 rarest plants have hedgerows and verges as their main habitat.

Hedges are thus a unique part of the countryside. I hope that this book will encourage readers to see for themselves some of the fascinating ways in which hedges have developed, and how the lives of the plants and animals they contain interact with each other. I also hope the reader will understand the reasons for the anxiety of wild life conservationists at the continuing threat to the very existence of our hedgerows.

Where a plant or animal is described in detail the scientific name is given in the text in addition to the common name. The scientific names of all the plants and animals mentioned in the book will be found in the index, following the common names.

1·Hedgerows Yesterday and Today

Those long, winding strips of woodland by the roads, lanes and fields are the last really big nature reserve we have, apart from the wild moors and lakes of our northern mountains and the seas around us. It has been estimated that the area of hedgerows in Britain—nearly 180,000 hectares (450,000 acres)—is twice that of the country's official nature reserves.

Hedges have been part of the landscape of the British Isles for at least a thousand years. Many hedges are mentioned as estate boundaries in Saxon documents and in some cases the hedges are still in exactly the same place as they were in the ninth and tenth century. However, most hedges were created largely in the years between 1750 and 1850, and like most aspects of our landscape which we accept as being 'natural' today, they were in fact man-made.

In order to understand how the hedges we know today came to be planted, it is helpful to take a brief look at the history of farming in Britain.

Men made their first big changes to the British landscape about 5,000 years ago when they began to clear the forests which then covered much of the country. They made small rectangular clearings surrounded by earth banks, and in these fields they grew wheat and barley. Sheep, cattle and pigs were also kept, but these Stone Age farmers were nomadic. As the land became exhausted in one place, they simply moved on. More permanent farms began to be developed around 1000 BC, and by the time the Roman invaders reached these shores, farming had become static.

1. A mosaic of hedgerows in Sussex

The 'open-field' system

During the Roman occupation of Britain more and more of the forest was cleared and eventually there were more than 1.5 million hectares (3.7 million acres) under cultivation. But after the Romans had left, at the beginning of the fifth century, the land was neglected and much of it went back to being a wilderness. When the Saxons began to settle in Britain 100 years later, they had to set about clearing the heavily wooded valleys.

The Saxons worked on the land with heavy ploughs drawn by teams of oxen. The large, open fields were divided up into strips about 200 metres long and 10 to 20 metres wide. Each strip was divided from the next by an open furrow, or bank, but never by a hedge. It was a shared system. Each farmer had several strips which were intermingled with those of his neighbours, so that no one had all the fertile or all the infertile land. The villagers shared the implements, and common land was set aside for grazing livestock. However, the villagers did not own the land. It all belonged to the lord of the manor and only this one man's land was permanently enclosed by hedges or drystone walls.

Traces of this 'open-field' system of farming can be seen in many parts of Britain. There are still fields whose surface appears to be folded into giant corrugations. The hollows between the bumps were once drainage ditches or footpaths between the strips of land.

Open-field farming continued while agriculture was a community effort and it was necessary to produce only enough food for the villagers. It remained common throughout the Middle Ages and lingered on in a few places until the end of the nineteenth century. Even today the land in the village of Laxton in Nottinghamshire is farmed on the open-field system.

The enclosure movement

The move towards enclosing the land had probably started by the twelfth and thirteenth centuries, when some woodland was cleared by individual peasants, who thus created new fields and farms. These new farmers were responsible for some hedgerows, made by pushing sticks into the ground to form stockades which took root and grew into hedges. Other hedgerows were created at this time when thin strips of trees and scrub were left round the edges of open fields as the woodlands were cleared. For this reason, many parish boundaries still contain very old woodlands and hedgerows.

Enclosing the open fields on a bigger scale began after a terrible outbreak of bubonic plague, the 'Black Death', had spread to England from the East in 1348. The population of the country was reduced by more than one-third and some villages had hardly anyone left alive. With the sudden reduction in population, there were not enough men to plough the land and sow the corn, so the lords of the manor let grass grow instead and kept many sheep on it in hedged enclosures which were large, even by modern standards. English wool was in great demand and much of it was sold to Flanders (Belgium). When so many sheep were kept, a large number of

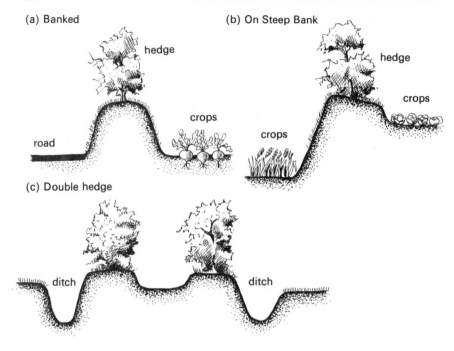

Fig. 1 Some of the many types of hedges

villagers had their strips of land taken away, and some villages were completely cleared of people and enclosed for sheep, even though technically such enclosure was illegal.

Enclosure continued on a piecemeal basis through the fifteenth and sixteenth centuries, although several more Acts of Parliament were passed to try to prevent the process. Even so, in England half the arable land was still unenclosed by 1700.

Most remaining villages were not enclosed until the eighteenth and nineteenth centuries, when the Industrial Revolution began and towns expanded and provided huge markets for farm produce. New methods of farming were developed in place of the inefficient strip system of cultivation, and more landlords saw that they could make a fortune from the land. Parliament passed a law whereby the owner could force the peasant to give up his strip of land, in exchange for a

(d) Double Ditched

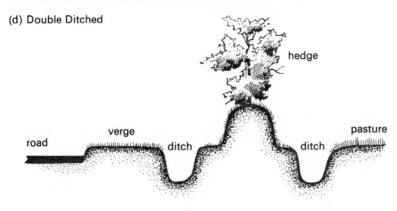

(e) Next to Stream

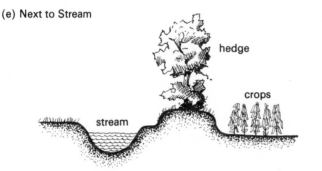

few pounds, or for some land, which was usually poorer, in another part of the estate.

Hedges were planted and the land was divided into fields. Sometimes several fields were let to farmers who could afford to pay a higher rent than before, and the owner farmed the rest of the land himself. Gradually the common land was enclosed too, some woods were cut down and neat plantations of trees took their place. The net result was that millions of hectares of farmland were now enclosed with hedges, and it is to these eighteenth- and nineteenth-century enclosures that we probably owe most of our hedges. The hedges planted at that time were, incidentally, usually straight in contrast to the sweeping curves of the earlier hedges, which often followed the line of valleys and other features of the landscape.

The move towards larger fields

For about 100 years the pattern of farming remained much the same, and then once again new agricultural techniques began to produce changes. Towards the end of the nineteenth century, new types of agricultural machinery and the use of wire fences led to the removal of many hedgerows to obtain larger fields. Then, in this century, the tractor replaced the horse, and even larger machines were developed, including the giant combine harvesters which can only operate efficiently in large fields. In parts of Britain, particularly some of the eastern counties, many farms already have huge prairie-like fields in which the new machines can operate. Farms are still growing in size and getting fewer in number.

Hedgerow removal

So convincing were the farmers' arguments for removing hedges that until November 1972 the Ministry of Agriculture actually provided a financial grant to help with the cost of hedgerow removal. No one knows for certain how many hedges have been lost, but it has been estimated that between 1946 and 1970 an average of 8000 km (5000 miles) of hedgerow were removed each year, which amounts to 200,000 km (125,000 miles) in the twenty-five-year period. The peak rate of removal was somewhere between 1960 and 1966, and since then it has fallen, particularly now that the Ministry of Agriculture's grant is no longer available.

Most of these hedges have been removed because of the need for larger fields to enable the modern machines to be used efficiently. Others have disappeared through neglect or accidental burning, often as a result of the deliberate firing of the stubble after corn crops have been harvested. Then there is the swallowing up of agricultural land, and hedges, for new roads, factories and houses.

Hedgerow management

Another major reason for the removal of hedges is the high cost of

2. A hedgerow in June. The verges are white with the flowers of cow parsley (*Anthriscus sylvestris*)

maintaining them, as compared with the long life and low maintenance costs of say a barbed wire fence. For there is a lot more to a
farmland hedge than merely planting a row of shrubs. Hedges are
made by bending over the saplings of the growing bush at an angle of
45 degrees. The bent saplings are woven round stakes driven into the
ground at intervals of 1 to 2 metres. The top is crowned by a tightly
woven layer of cut sticks, known as hethers, which stop the growing
wood from springing upright, and unwanted twigs and branches are
removed. And to prevent it from running wild, a hedge needs this
skilled, expensive and time-consuming treatment every five to ten
years. In addition, the coarse vegetation at the bottom of a well

managed hedge is often brushed out every year and the sides are given a light clipping.

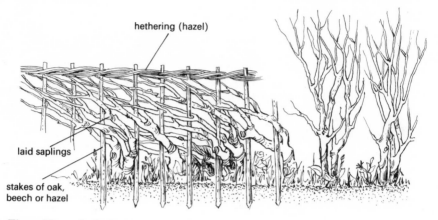

Fig. 2 How a hedge is laid

Other benefits from hedgerows

It is important to remember that hedges were originally planted by farmers as barriers, as a means of keeping their animals in, and as a means of separating one farmer's land, and livestock, from another's. Of course, once the hedges had been planted, they were used for other purposes. They provided shelter from the weather for man and his animals. To a limited extent, they were used as a source of bean and pea sticks, spars for thatching, walking-sticks, poles for hurdles, and firewood, as well as providing blackberries, nuts and other wild foods. Hedges also proved to be useful to the field sportsman. They offer nesting sites for pheasants and partridges and also the wild plants and insects on which they feed. When these game birds are being driven along in front of the guns, hedges force them to rise up into the air so that they make a better target. In fox-hunting districts, well-laid hedges make excellent jumps to test the riders' skill.

In mild but windy districts hedges shelter valuable horticultural crops and protect them from blemishes, enabling the crop to be sold earlier than would otherwise be the case. The tiny daffodil fields of

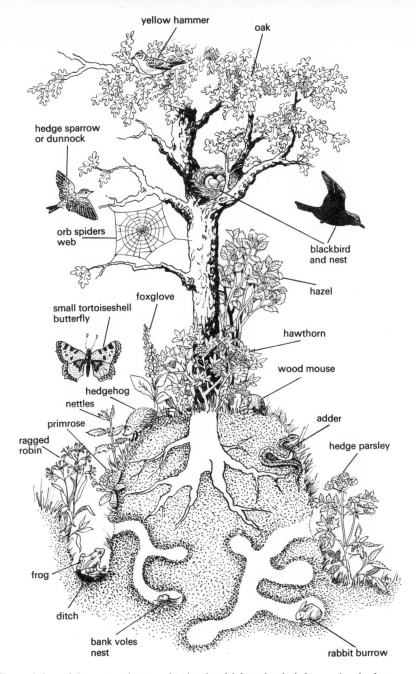

Fig. 3 A few of the many plants and animals which make their homes in a hedgerow.

the Scilly Isles and parts of Cornwall are sheltered from the winter gales by hedges up to six metres high. The fields are made tiny not only to obtain the maximum shelter from the high hedges but also because the hedges allow a slight rise of temperature in the fields which makes the bulbs flower earlier. The valuable hop gardens of Kent and Sussex, Worcestershire and Herefordshire are sheltered by tall hedges of hawthorn and other species. In areas where the soil is light and sandy, hedges can prevent the soil from being blown away in dry windy weather. However, it is rather ironic that in one district in Britain where erosion by windblow is a serious problem, there are virtually no hedges and never have been. This is the fenland of East Anglia, but even here some willow hedges have been planted in recent years as defence against the increasing problems of 'fen blow'.

A tall hedge can protect the motorist from strong cross-winds and drifting snow and, in those few sections of dual-carriageway roads where hedges are planted along the central reservation, motorists are shielded from oncoming headlights at night, and have a springy crash-barrier should a vehicle go out of control.

Like so many of the other products of ancient craftsmen, hedges fulfil their functions very well and at the same time are extremely beautiful. In the best kinds of hedge, plants and animals exist in highly complex relationships with one another and are normally in balance with man's activities around them. In the next few chapters we shall look at some of the ways in which hedgerow plants and animals live, and the way in which they react with each other.

2·Hedgerow Plants

Two thousand years ago vast forests covered the greater part of the British Isles, so that in some ways woodland can be considered the most natural vegetation of Britain. Because of this, the animals of this country, and particularly its bird and insect life, originated mainly in woodland. However, virtually none of our existing woodland is natural; all has been interfered with by man to a greater or lesser degree. As I said in the last chapter, in order to create fields where they could grow their crops and keep their animals, early men made clearings in the forest, and the woodland animals had to adapt to these new conditions as best they could.

How hedges were formed

Some of our present-day hedges were left behind as thin boundary strips when the rest of the woodland was cleared. Others began life as boundaries around the edges of woodland, planted with shrubs from the wood itself.

Still more hedges developed from the scrub which grew along the previously unhedged boundaries between the fields or field strips, in some cases from sticks which were pushed into the ground to form fences, and later took root. Other hedges began as the typical planted rows of one or more shrub species.

Almost accidentally, from man's point of view, as the hedgerows developed they started to be colonised by a great variety of wildlife. The hedges helped to compensate for the loss of the woodlands, because they were very similar in nature to the woodland edge, where most animal species originally lived.

Hedgerow trees and shrubs

Whichever way a hedge was formed, there are not many kinds of trees and shrubs which can tolerate the rough treatment to which hedges are subjected when they are trimmed and layered to form a thick barrier that will keep in horses, cattle and sheep. The most usual ones are hawthorn, blackthorn, elm, beech, hazel, maple, ash, elder, and privet.

Of course, every shrub that can be used to make a hedge has been used somewhere or other. In parts of the Breckland of Norfolk and Suffolk the hedges are of pine or spruce; holly hedges dominate parts of Staffordshire and elm the Isle of Sheppey off the Kent coast. Beech hedges are numerous around the edges of Exmoor, while at Meikleour in Perthshire there is a famous beech hedge which is one-third of a mile long and 27 metres high. In a few districts there are long hedges that are almost purely golden-yellow laburnum, while in western Ireland, parts of Devon and Cornwall, and the Channel Islands, one may find hedges of crimson fuchsia. On the Lizard peninsula of Cornwall there are evergreen hedges of feathery branched tamarisk, a shrub introduced to the coasts of England and Wales from the Mediterranean.

But these are exceptional hedges, introduced in a number of cases from abroad. Generally it is the toughest native shrubs and trees that make up our hedges, the species that from earliest times farmers have been able to grow most easily.

Hawthorn hedges

The commonest hedgerow shrub of all is the hawthorn or quick-thorn. In order to form a hedge, the red hawthorn berries, or 'haws', are gathered in autumn and stored in damp sand for eighteen months before they will germinate. The seeds are then sown and the seedlings allowed to grow for two years. They can then be transplanted to another bed, with more room between the seedlings, and a year later they are usually cut off near the ground to encourage strong roots and a more bushy top growth. After this has developed the young shrubs can be planted out at distances between 10 cm and 1 metre apart, but for a few years they need protection by temporary fences, and to begin with, weeding is necessary.

Under natural conditions, hawthorn seedlings spring up frequently where birds have deposited the hard seeds that have passed through their bodies. Only the fleshy outer layer of the fruit is digested; the seeds pass out unharmed in the bird's droppings.

On the thin dark twigs of hawthorn, with its small pinkish buds, many shoots take the form of sharp thorns, which makes hawthorn a valuable barrier against the movement of man and beast. The leaves, bright green in spring, duller later, are deeply lobed. Clusters of

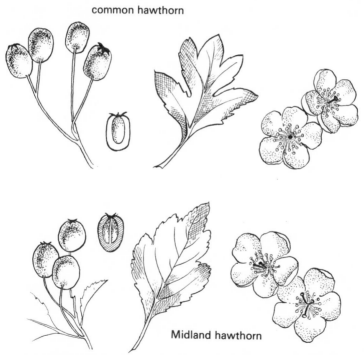

common hawthorn

Midland hawthorn

Fig. 4 The common hawthorn (*Crataegus monogyna*) and the Midland hawthorn (*Crataegus laevigata*)

flowers are borne in May, hence the alternative name for the hawthorn, May blossom. Each flower has five white petals, many stamens and a central ovary. This ripens by October to a red berry which attracts birds, especially members of the thrush family, finches and tits. The haws are also an important food for the wood mouse and other small mammals.

There are two species of hawthorn in Britain. The common hawthorn (*Crataegus monogyna*) is found all over the British Isles, except for quite large areas of north Scotland which are without it. It has only one hard seed inside each haw. The Midland hawthorn (*Crataegus laevigata*), is found chiefly in the east Midlands and south-east England, but is absent from most of Wales, north England, Scotland and Ireland. The Midland hawthorn has two or three seeds in each haw, and beautiful red- and pink-flowered varieties of it are grown as ornamental shrubs. Though a few hedges are composed of the Midland hawthorn, it is mainly found growing in oak woodlands.

The soil and hedgerow shrubs

Exactly what species of shrubs you may find in a hedge depends very much on whether or not you are standing on calcareous soil, that is soil containing calcium carbonate in the form of chalk or limestone. If you are, then the hedges are likely to contain maple, common buckthorn, dogwood, traveller's joy, guelder rose and sweet-briar. There may also be occasional bushes of spindle, barberry and wayfaring tree. Perhaps the most conspicuous of these plants which thrive on chalk or limestone is the traveller's joy (*Clematis vitalba*) or, as it is sometimes called, because of the white feathery fruiting heads, 'old man's beard'. This climbing shrub grows only on calcareous soils, and so sensitive is it to the presence of calcium carbonate in the soil that, from a car or train window, you can often tell exactly where the soil changes in composition, merely by the presence or absence of traveller's joy.

Away from chalk and limestone, the hedgerow plant species are always much fewer. But on practically all lowland farm soils, the commonest species are generally hawthorn, hazel, holly, bramble, elder, willow, crab apple, blackthorn, wild roses, honeysuckle and ivy.

Dating a hedgerow

On whatever type of soil they are growing, one of the chief features of most of our hedges is their variety, and sometimes the number of different species to be found along a length of hedge is quite remarkable. Most of the hedges planted about two hundred years ago are pure hawthorn and show little variation, but earlier hedges dating from Elizabethan times, though they may once have been pure hawthorn, are now colonized by many species. However, the Saxon hedges that remain are the richest of all.

3. Dogwood (*Thelycrania sanguinea*), a common hedgerow shrub, particularly on calcarous soils

These observations led Dr. Max Hooper, working for the Natural Environment Research Station at Monks Wood Experimental Station in Cambridgeshire, to develop an interesting theory: that the greater the variety of shrubs growing in a hedge, the older the hedge must be. This theory is based on the likely belief that whoever first planted hedges used only one or two different species. Then, whatever the species of shrub originally planted, others gradually spread to the hedgerow, arriving as seeds being carried by birds, mammals and the wind, until a hedgerow of mixed shrubs, trees and other wild plants became established.

This theory has been tested by the scientists from Monks Wood Experimental Station, using 30-metre stretches of a large number of hedges whose age can be confirmed by consulting ancient documents. It turned out that there was roughly one species of shrub in the hedges for every 100 years of their age. Of course it must be remembered that this is a very rough measure, since there are obvious local differences in climate, soil and the way the hedge has been managed which will affect the number of species present. Hedges which were left after woodland was cleared may well contain many shrub species, but they are usually much older than planted hedges in any case. The figure of one species per 100 years may also not hold good where there is much woodland in the neighbourhood of the hedge, from which rapid colonisation by shrubs could occur, or where the climate is harsh or the soil unsuitable. But generally this is a good rule of thumb.

If you want to date a hedge in your area, it is not sufficient simply to count the number of tree and shrub species in a 30-metre stretch. You should first of all be careful how you choose the section of hedge. The ends of hedges may give a completely inaccurate result, particularly if they join a wood or copse. The simplest and safest way to choose a typical section of hedge is to walk a set distance from one end, say ten paces, and then record the number of tree and shrub species, including wild roses, in the next 30 metres of hedge as seen from *one side*. Make sure you have the landowner's permission before going on to private land and only count established woody shrubs and trees; ignore seedlings and also exclude climbers and stragglers such as honeysuckle and brambles. The more 30-metre lengths of the hedge you can check the better, but often it will only be reasonable to look at three or four. Then if, for example, you find that your study of these lengths of hedge gives you an average of five tree and shrub species, then your hedge is roughly 500 years old. Of course, if you can look up old records (page 123), then you may find out more interesting facts about how the hedge came to be planted and be able to date it more accurately.

'Woodland relic' hedges

It was mentioned earlier in this chapter that some hedges have arisen as a result of the clearance of all but a thin strip of woodland, or by planting a hedge around a wood, using species from within the wood. The scientists at Monks Wood Experimental Station have found that of the shrubs present in these 'woodland relic' hedges, hazel, spindle, maple and dogwood all occurred much more frequently than in planted hedges. The trees and shrubs which colonised planted hedges turned out to be blackthorn, rose, ash, and elder, with smaller amounts of privet and maple.

As well as trees and shrubs, a number of woodland herbs were also common in 'woodland relic' hedges. Of these the most abundant was dog's mercury (*Mercurialis perennis*), but other well known plants included bluebell (*Endymion non-scriptus*), primrose (*Primula vulgaris*), wood anemone (*Anemone nemorosa*), wood spurge (*Euphorbia amygdaloides*) and yellow archangel (*Galeobdolon luteum*).

Other hedgerow plants

Of course many other plant species have been recorded in hedgerows, something like five or six hundred altogether. But only about half of these occur sufficiently frequently for them to be thought of as hedgerow plants, and practically all of them are found in other habitats, such as woodland or grassland.

The smaller plants to be found in a hedgerow are in competition with each other for two interdependent necessities, light and support,

4. Primroses (*Primula vulgaris*)

and for this reason climbing and shade-loving species are numerous. Exactly which species grow depends on how the hedge is managed: hedges running from north to south, that is facing east and west, generally are richer in plant life than those running in other directions. The type of soil and the way in which the hedge is 'built' are also important. Some hedges are on level ground, others are growing on a bank standing well above the adjoining ground on one or both sides. The hedge may be edged on one or both sides by a water-containing ditch; it may be next to a stream, a dry road, woodland, moorland, heath or cultivated ground.

Climbers and scramblers growing through on their way to the light include honeysuckle (*Lonicera periclymenum*), field bindweed (*Convolvulus arvensis*), great bindweed (*Calystegia sepium*) and hop (*Humulus lupulus*), all with twining stems; traveller's joy or old man's beard (*Clematis vitalba*) with twining leaf stalks; the vetches with leaf tendrils, white bryony (*Bryonia dioica*) with large spring-like tendrils, ivy (*Hedera helix*) with adhesive roots; dog rose (*Rosa canina*), brambles, and goosegrass or cleavers ʼ(*Galium aparine*), which scramble by means of thorns and hooks.

Many of the non-climbing flowering plants which live within the shade have either long and narrow or much divided leaves: they are thus able to make the most of the narrow shafts of light which penetrate the upper foliage. Others present are definitely shade-loving species, such as sweet violet (*Viola odorata*), primrose (*Primula vulgaris*), ground ivy (*Glechoma hederacea*) and cuckoo pint (*Arum maculatum*). Where the shade atmosphere is moist, ferns are prominent, hart's tongue fern (*Phyllitis scolopendrium*), being often very conspicuous, especially in the west of the British Isles. On damp hedgebanks mosses and liverworts, small green plants similar in structure to mosses, may carpet the ground, while in the western parts of Britain mosses, liverworts and lichens may even clothe the trunks and branches of hedgerow shrubs and trees to a height of several metres. These same trees may also have a fern, the polypody (*Polypodium vulgare*) growing on them. These plants which grow on

5. The hop (*Humulus lupulus*), once a common hedgerow climbing plant, is now becoming rare

shrubs and trees are called *epiphytes*: they obtain their water either
directly from rain or from water vapour in the atmosphere; their
mineral salts are obtained either from the bark of the tree, or from
dust washed down by the rain.

Grass verges

Our survey of the hedgerow vegetation must also include a brief look
at the grass verges which so often bound hedges, particularly those by
roadsides. There is very little semi-natural permanent grassland left
in Britain. Most of the meadows and pastures we see are what are
called grass leys. They are temporary grasslands which are regularly
ploughed and resown with artificial mixtures of grass and clover seed.
In many districts the only semi-natural grassland remaining lies in
strips along the edges of both grass and arable fields, next to those
hedges which remain, and on the roadsides. The actual species
present depend upon the subsoil and humidity, so that foxgloves

6. A grass verge in spring, showing the way in which the leaves arrange themselves
so as to trap the maximum amount of light. The flowers are those of silverweed
(*Potentilla anserina*), a common plant of roadsides and verges

(*Digitalis purpurea*) appear in the acid verge, but cowslips (*Primula veris*) may turn up where there is chalk. A dry stretch may contain wild thyme (*Thymus drucei*), whereas ferns grow in a wet one. If the verge is examined in the spring and summer it may be a riot of colour produced by the blooms of meadow cranesbill (*Geranium pratense*), and bird's foot trefoil (*Lotus corniculatus*). This is why naturalists so much dislike the unnecessary spraying of roadsides with weedkiller or the too frequent cutting of grass verges.

Producers and consumers

Finally, we must consider the inter-relationships between the plants in the hedgerow and the animals present. All green plants contain the green substance chlorophyll, which is used to trap the energy of sunlight. Once the sun's energy has been absorbed by the plant it is used to combine carbon dioxide from the air with water, to make food substances such as sugar and starch. These materials, which are rich in energy, travel from the leaves where they are made to the other parts of the plant.

However, animals do not have chlorophyll, nor do some plants such as mushrooms, toadstools and other fungi. If living things do not have chlorophyll, they cannot make their own food. Instead they have to rely on living green plants, or their dead and dying remains, for food and energy. As green plants provide food for all other organisms they are often called *producers*. The animals which feed upon green plants either directly or indirectly are called *consumers*.

All living things are linked together, because every living thing depends on another for food. These food links between organisims are known as food chains, but it should be noticed that all food chains begin with green plants. Any change in the numbers of a green plant will affect the populations of all the animals in the food chains which begin with that plant species. The animals and plants at the start of a food chain are always numerous and often very small. Moving along the chain, the numbers of animals decrease as their size increases. This is best shown by a pyramid of numbers, which represents the relative numbers of organisms involved at various points along a food

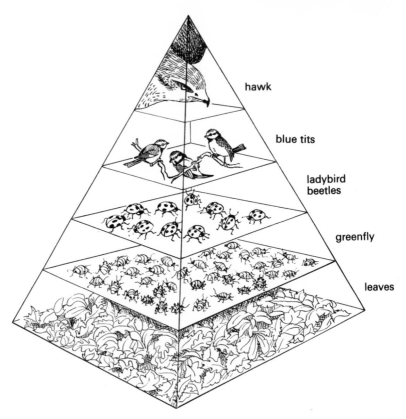

hawk

blue tits

ladybird
beetles

greenfly

leaves

Fig. 5 A pyramid of numbers, showing the relative numbers of organisms involved
at various points along a food chain

chain. Provided that the 'balance of nature' shown by the pyramid of
numbers is maintained—that is, if the plants are always more
numerous than the plant-eaters, and these are more numerous than
the predators—the food chain will remain unbroken. If the balance is
disturbed, as when a hedgerow is destroyed, the animals affected
must either find food elsewhere, or die.

3·The Bird Life of Hedgerows

Hedgerows and bird life

It is the hedgerows that give variety to the bird life of farmland and gardens. Few birds nest in hedgeless fields except skylarks, partridges, lapwings, and in some districts corn buntings. The hedges give shelter to many of the garden birds, and to two species especially characteristic of the English country lane, but rarely seen in gardens, the yellowhammer and whitethroat. Hedgerow trees also bring in nesting rooks, carrion crows and magpies.

As has been emphasised earlier, deciduous woodland was the original and natural vegetation of much of the British Isles, and most of the bird species we have are those which were originally woodland species. Blackbirds, thrushes, robins, tits, warblers, woodpeckers and pigeons, and most of our other familiar birds, a total of about forty species, all once depended entirely on trees and shrubs for food or shelter or both. Gardens and the vast network of hedges which cover most of lowland Britain and Ireland provide birds with a substitute woodland; so what man has taken away by clearing the forests he has to some extent restored by planting hedges and garden shrubs and trees.

Plant-eating insects in hedges are food for many insectivorous birds including tits, tree creepers, wrens, robins, thrushes, blackbirds and summer visitors such as the whitethroat and other warblers. Many seed-eating birds also catch insects and other hedgerow invertebrates to supplement the diet of their rapidly growing young. Fortunately the breeding season of our birds

coincides with the spring and summer months, when the hedgerows
are teeming with insects.

The hedgerow also provides a plentiful supply of food for the seed-
eaters—grass seeds for linnets, thistle seeds for goldfinches, ash seeds

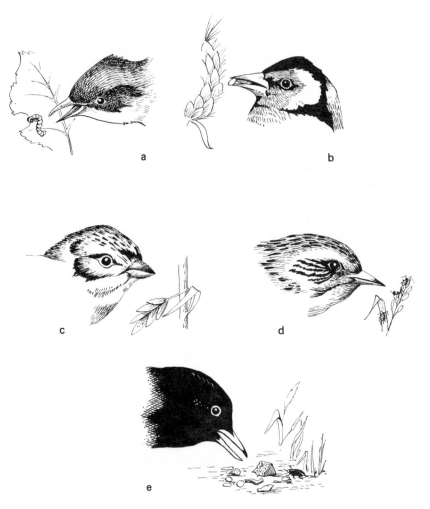

Fig. 6 The beaks of some hedgerow birds
(a) whitethroat—insect-eater (b) goldfinch—seed-eater (c) yellow hammer—seed-
eater (d) hedge sparrow or dunnock—insect-eater (e) blackbird—varied diet

for bullfinches. In winter, hedgerow berries and seeds help many birds to survive, including two winter migrants, the redwing and fieldfare, both of which eat rose hips, haws, the fruit of the hawthorn, and other berries. If the hedgerow fruits are important for the survival of many birds over the winter, these birds in turn are important dispersal agents for the hedgerow shrubs. They take the seeds from one hedge and release them in their droppings in another, perhaps several miles away.

Finches, buntings and sparrows also congregate in flocks in winter to feed on fruit, seeds or anything else they can find. The tendency of these small birds to flock together in this way is probably a means of defence against birds of prey, several species of which regularly search along the hedgerow for food.

Most species of birds roost in bushes and trees, where they are relatively safe from predators. Hedges and hedgerow trees provide good roosting sites as well as places where birds can hide during the day.

Among birds which weave their nests in the dense, tangled bushes or the thick ground vegetation of a hedgerow are long-tailed tits, robins, wrens, hedge sparrows, blackbirds, thrushes, wood pigeons, chaffinches, pheasants and partridges. It is estimated that about 10 million birds now nest in our hedgerows every year.

Hedgerows, and particularly hedgerow trees, also provide another necessity for bird life. All the British land birds have a territory, an area of ground which they defend against other members of their own species. It is the male bird which does most of the advertising of the territory by displaying, threatening and singing, or all three. In order to throw their voices the greatest distance and warn off rivals, a number of small birds make use of a song post which is taller than the general level of the territory. Many hedgerow trees and shrubs which are higher than average provide the necessary vantage points for male songsters, while others sing from within the bushes in the hedge itself.

SOME COMMON HEDGEROW BIRDS

adapted from Hedges *by E. Pollard, M. D. Hooper and*
N. W. Moore. Collins 1974

Part of hedgerow	Nest only	Nest and Feed	Feed only
Upper branches of hedgerow trees	Carrion crow Rook	Wood pigeon Greenfinch	Blue tit Chaffinch
Trunks and holes in trees	Barn owl Little owl Stock dove Jackdaw Great tit Blue tit Starling Tree sparrow	Wren (in ivy)	Tree creeper
Shrubs	Turtle dove Magpie	Wood pigeon Cuckoo Long-tailed tit Song thrush Blackbird Lesser whitethroat Hedge sparrow Wren Goldfinch Linnet Lesser redpoll Bullfinch Chaffinch Greenfinch House sparrow	Fieldfare Redwing Mistle thrush Robin Great tit Marsh tit Blue tit Whitethroat
Herbs, low bushes and brambles		Whitethroat Yellow-hammer Reed bunting	Goldfinch Greenfinch
Ground	Skylark	Robin Corn bunting Pheasant Partridge Red-legged partridge	Hedge sparrow Blackbird Song thrush Wren

Mapping a territory

It is possible to map a bird's territory if you begin patient and careful observations in the early spring when the birds are first taking up residence. Robins behave in an unusual way in that they occupy a territory, although not always the same one, throughout the year.

Begin by drawing a sketch map of your hedge and neighbouring roads, fields and gardens (Fig. 7). Mark on it the spots where a particular bird is regularly seen singing. Robins, blackbirds, song thrushes, great tits and chaffinches have a strong territorial instinct and it is a good idea to begin with one of these species. Mark on the map the points where other birds are driven off. Note the birds against which your chosen individual reacts, and those it ignores. Record the bird's behaviour during the day, and how the male behaves towards the females. Gradually a clear picture of the extent

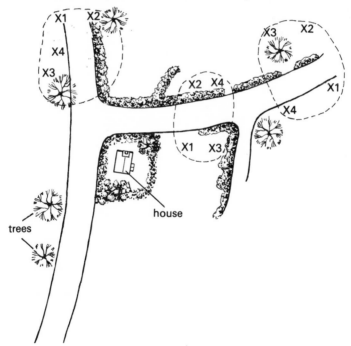

Fig. 7 Mapping the territories of blackbirds in a country lane

of the bird's territory will emerge and other aspects of its fighting and courtship behaviour may be observed. Repeat this type of study with other common species.

Another method of discovering the extent of a bird's territory is to use a stuffed member of the same species. This can sometimes be bought from a junk shop for a few pence. If you can obtain a stuffed robin, for example, and move it about in and near another robin's territory, you will be able to see exactly where it is attacked and where it is left alone, and plot the bird's territory quite accurately. However, it is important that you do not carry out this observation during the breeding season, when you may cause the resident birds to leave the eggs to chill or their young to starve.

Common hedgerow birds

The commonest hedgerow birds are undoubtedly the blackbird, hedge sparrow, chaffinch, robin, whitethroat, song thrush and yellow-hammer, together with pigeons, jackdaws, rooks, house sparrows and linnets. Three species of game birds are also closely associated with hedgerows and in many areas are abundant. These are pheasant, common partridge and red-legged partridge. Nesting partridges dislike seeing others of their own kind and so the more their view is interrupted by hedges and shrubs, the more nest territories can occur in a given area.

Exactly which bird species are present in a hedgerow depends both on the kinds of trees and shrubs present and on the way these are managed by the farmer. Unless the hedge is allowed to remain thick at the bottom, hedge sparrows, robins and wrens are unlikely to be found. It is essential that old trees such as oak and ash are left standing in the hedge, particularly when they are dead or dying, if hole-nesting birds such as jackdaws, starlings, great tits, tree sparrows, little owls and stock doves are to nest there. When scrambling brambles and tall herbs are removed from a hedge, whitethroats, yellow-hammers and reed buntings are almost certain to be absent.

Indeed, while any hedge is better than no hedge, the researchers at

7. Hen pheasant (*Phasianus colchicus*), well camouflaged as she incubates her eggs at the foot of a hedge

Monks Wood Experimental Station in Cambridgeshire have shown that hedges with good ground cover are much more favourable for birds than those without it. By far and away the best hedge of all is the thick, overgrown one, although unfortunately this is the type of hedge least liked by farmers. No one seems to have investigated whether the presence of ditches or banks makes a hedge more or less favourable for birds, although clearly they must have some effect. This is an ideal subject for the patient naturalist to investigate.

The exact importance of hedgerows themselves to birds has in recent years been investigated by a number of researchers. Mention was made in Chapter 1 of Laxton in Nottinghamshire which is one of the very few parishes in lowland England which has never been enclosed by hedges. On its farmland there are no trees or bushes; apart from the crops there are only grass ridges and ditches. When the scientists carried out a survey of the bird life of Laxton they found that only the bird species of open fields were present—mainly skylarks, partridges and lapwings. Most of the ordinary farmland

birds were absent, although they were common in those parts of
the surrounding countryside which have been enclosed by hedges.

The hedge sparrow or dunnock

To return to the birds of the hedgerows, the hedge sparrow (*Prunella
modularis*) is probably the most typical species, even if the blackbird
is the most numerous. But unlike the blackbird, which often feeds
away from hedges, even if it nests in them, the hedge sparrow
depends upon the hedge (or woodland margin) for both shelter and
much of its food. The hedge sparrow often looks more like a mouse as
it scuttles about in the hedge bottom, but its faint piping call, which
can be heard throughout most of the year, gives its presence away.
Although it is called a hedge sparrow, this small dull brown bird is
not a sparrow at all. It has the typical sharp, thin bill of an insect-
eater, as distinct from the stout bill of the seed-eating house and tree
sparrows. However, the dunnock, as many prefer to call the hedge
sparrow, survives the winter largely on small seeds, such as those of
grasses and small plants, when the insects it picks from the leaf litter
and bushes in summer are not available.

The dunnock is also one of the common victims of the cuckoo,

Fig. 8 Hedge sparrow or dunnock feeding a young cuckoo

although no one really knows why this should be. Its four or five pale blue eggs are rarely matched in size or colour by those of the much larger cuckoo, and as the young cuckoo grows rapidly, from about 7 g to more than 340 g in three weeks, it pushes out the young dunnocks from the mossy nest to their death. Even so, dunnocks are numerous and tame in gardens, parks, hedgerows and woodland, and a recent survey by the British Trust for Ornithology estimated that there are more than four dunnocks to the hectare on farmland in England.

Bullfinches

Much more handsome than the dunnock is the bullfinch (*Pyrrhula pyrrhula*), although it is not always as welcome. Like the other finches, it has the stout, short bill of a seed-eating bird, but unlike its equally striking relatives, including the goldfinch, chaffinch, greenfinch and redpoll, which also feed and nest in hedgerows, the bullfinch does not always stick to seeds. Bullfinches were originally birds of woodland, and their main foods are the seeds of trees, particularly ash, which occurs in both hedges and woods. Unfortunately the crop of ash seeds fails about every second year and many bullfinches take to orchards, where they can ruin a crop by stripping the early buds of fruit trees. One bullfinch was seen to eat the buds of a plum tree at the rate of thirty a minute. For some unknown reason, since the mid-1950s, the numbers of bullfinches has increased enormously, and in some areas they are no longer protected by law. But even in fruit-growing districts the bullfinch also takes large quantities of weed seeds as well as feeding its young on caterpillars, many of which are harmful to plants grown for human food.

Blackbirds

The abundant and widely distributed blackbird (*Turdus merula*), is also not always without blame, since it will on occasion turn to soft fruit crops for nourishment, although its main items of food are insects and their larvae, earthworms and wild fruits and berries.

Much of the blackbird's success in colonising new habitats in the past 100 years must be due to its willingness to sample new kinds of food, including table scraps, and to the fact that it is willing to build its nest on a variety of sites from ground level to 14 metres high.

The blackbird's nest is a solid, cup-shaped structure of grasses, roots, mosses and twigs, reinforced with mud and then lined with more fine grasses. In this it often manages to rear four broods of three to five young in a season. It is not surprising, then, that the blackbird is considered to be our most common resident breeding bird, with over 10 million of them in the British Isles. Added to which, a substantial number of immigrant blackbirds from the Continent overwinter in Britain.

Birds' nests

It is the woodland and former woodland birds, such as the blackbird, that build the most elaborate nests. And of course, large numbers of these nests are now to be found in our hedgerows.

Song thrushes, chaffinches and many other species build cosy cup-shaped nests, like those of the blackbird in shape but differing in size and building materials. A few other woodland or former woodland

8. Blackbird (*Turdus merula*)

Fig. 9 Some hedgerow birds' nests
(a) song thrush (b) wren (c) long-tailed tit (d) magpie (e) wood pigeon

birds gain added protection by building a dome over the cup. House sparrows, and very occasionally tree sparrows, do this when they nest in the open; magpies protect the cup with a dome of sorts by giving it a canopy of twigs. Wrens, willow warblers, wood warblers and chiffchaffs build more intricate domes; but none can vie with the long-tailed tit's beautifully-made 'bottle' of lichen-covered moss, with the entrance hole near the top. At the other extreme, though, mention must be made of two other bird species which often breed in hedgerows but which can by no means be considered architects.

The female wood pigeon (*Columba palumbus*), builds a flat platform of twigs in which it lays its two white eggs. So fragile and flimsy is this nest that the eggs and young can frequently be seen from the ground below. But if the eggs or young do fall right through the nest, the pigeon is usually able to produce more, since it has been known to breed in any month of the year, although most commonly in August and September.

The female cuckoo (*Cuculus canorus*), already mentioned in connection with the dunnock on page 48, goes one better by not building a nest at all. She ensures the continuation of her species by removing an egg from each host's nest and laying one of her own in its place, until she has a clutch of twelve or thirteen eggs scattered about her territory.

Scavengers

In the hedgerow, as well as the seed-eating and insect-eating birds mentioned earlier, there is a group of scavengers, consisting of certain members of the crow family. Typical of these, and most numerous in hedgerows, is the magpie (*Pica pica*), whose diet consists partly of carrion, including the bodies of animals killed in road accidents. Magpies also rob other birds, including pheasants and partridges, of their eggs and young, which does not make them very popular with gamekeepers. But like all bird species which thrive in spite of persecution, the magpie will eat a variety of foods, including insects, seeds, fruits and small mammals.

9. Magpie (*Pica pica*), a hedgerow scavenger

Birds of prey

Besides the scavengers, there are birds which feed predominantly on small animals which they catch alive. Kestrels, sparrowhawks and some owls will visit hedgerows in search of their prey. Barn owls (*Tyto alba*), are sometimes seen, looking almost ghostly white, in car headlights at night as they fly silently over hedgerows, verges and neighbouring fields in search of their prey. Their hooked beaks are typical of those of birds of prey, and are used for tearing up the flesh of their victims, which include mice, voles, rats, shrews, moles, small birds, beetles and moths. The indigestible fur and bones of their victims are coughed up and ejected via the beak in the form of pellets. During the past few years, the barn owl, sparrowhawk and other birds of prey have started to increase in numbers, after the serious decline which came about when insecticides and other poisons began to build up in their bodies through eating food contaminated by these chemicals.

Another bird of prey which visits hedges, and sometimes nests in holes in old hedgerow trees, and occasionally in disused rabbit burrows, is the little owl (*Athene noctua*). The dark grey- and white-streaked bird is only about 22 cm long. It was first introduced into Kent and Northamptonshire from the Continent in the early nineteenth century and rapidly spread over England and Wales into the southern counties of Scotland. It can be seen by day, perched on a telegraph pole or wire, or on an old roadside tree. If disturbed, it flies off with an undulating flight rather like that of a woodpecker. The little owl feeds mainly on insects, including earwigs, beetles and craneflies, as well as taking some mice, voles, young rats and other small mammals, doing most of its hunting at dusk and dawn.

A study of bird pellets

The little owl, like the barn owl and all other birds of prey, produces pellets of undigested food. But these pellets are also produced by many other birds—more than sixty species—including gulls, rooks, crows, herons and a number of small birds such as robins and flycatchers. If you can identify the bird which produced the pellets, you can make many interesting discoveries about the food of that species by dissecting the pellets.

The pellets are by no means the nasty, smelly or messy things that you might expect, bearing in mind where they have come from. They are a bit damp when produced, but they dry quickly and are then quite inoffensive. Nevertheless, do wash your hands thoroughly after handling the pellets or, better still, wear rubber gloves.

The first task is to soak the pellets in warm water for an hour or two. Then pour the water away, and place a pellet on a piece of clean blotting paper or several layers of newspaper. Gently tease out the pellet with a pair of forceps or two mounted needles. Try to separate the various types of material in the pellets into little heaps—the bones of animals in one heap, the fur, feathers or vegetable matter into another, the wing-cases and legs of insects into a third, and so on.

When you have done this, you can go on to examine the contents of the heaps more carefully, and this is where a good hand lens is useful. Do not worry if you cannot at first identify every bone or insect part.

This will come by experience, and a visit to an expert naturalist or a museum will help greatly. One job you can do is to put all the limb bones, ribs, shoulder bones and vertebrae (the bones of the spine) into separate heaps. Bird skulls are easy to recognise, since the beak usually remains attached. The skulls of mice, voles and other rodents can be identified by the large front teeth (incisors) adapted for gnawing; the skulls of shrews and moles can be recognized by the more even and sharply pointed teeth necessary for gripping and chewing insects, worms and other invertebrates.

If you want to make a permanent record of your work, then the material must be dried thoroughly. A piece of card of a suitable size will be necessary, and on this you can stick with glue, first a whole

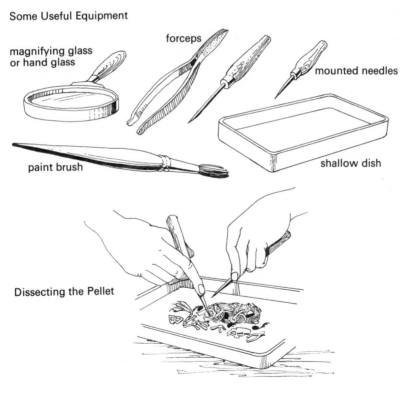

Fig. 10 Dissection of an owl's pellet

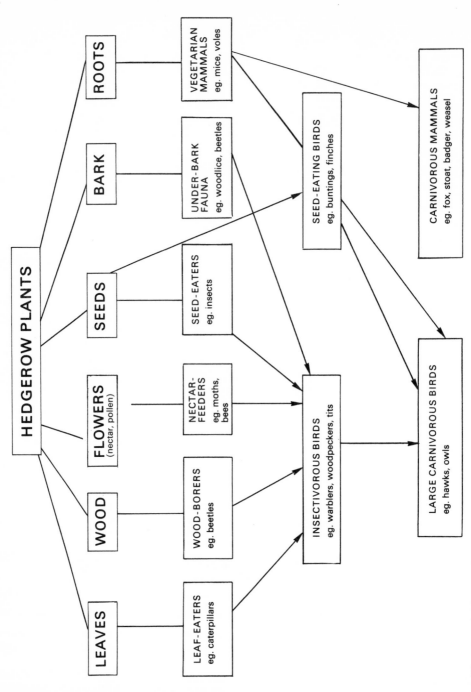

Fig. 11 A hedgerow food web

pellet of the type you have been dissecting, next a specimen of the 'binding' material—the fur, feathers or vegetable matter, and finally a selection of the bones and insect remains that you have separated out. This done, write on the card details about the pellet, including the species of bird which produced it, where and when it was found and the identity, as far as possible, of the parts which made up the pellet. You can then go on to repeat this process with the pellets of other species until you have a representative collection. At the same time you will be learning a great deal about the way in which the various plant and animal species are linked together in food chains.

Food webs

If you had not realised it already, your work on bird pellets will soon show you that food chains are an over-simplification of what really happens in nature. The food chain is shown as a straight line, but in reality the feeding relationships between organisms are much more complicated. We might trace out the following food chain:

$$grass \longrightarrow field\ vole \longrightarrow barn\ owl$$

But many animals feed on grass besides voles, while voles, as we shall see in the next chapter, may feed on other plants besides grasses. Voles can be the prey of weasels and other predators. In their turn, voles, owls and weasels may have fleas and other parasites on their bodies. And as well as water and sunlight, the grass needs the mineral salts which come from the waste products and decay of living organisms for its survival. Clearly in real life food chains are not simple 'straight lines', but each organism may link and be part of many other food chains. This more complicated relationship is known as a *food web* and, within it, each organism is competing for its life requirements with those members of its own and other species. With so many species in competition it may seem surprising that any sort of balance or equilibrium should develop between them at all. But we should not be surprised that quite small changes in a habitat such as a hedgerow can trigger off a chain reaction that may destroy this balance.

4 · Mammals of the Hedgerow

There are relatively few mammal species in the British Isles, and some of these are rare. Most wild mammals are difficult to observe because they tend to keep to the undergrowth and so many of them come out mainly at night. Nevertheless, nearly half of our native land mammal species live in hedgerows and almost all use hedges at some time or another, if only to obtain shelter and protection as they move from one area to another, or cover as they stalk their prey.

Wood mice

Of all our land mammals, the most common and widespread is the wood mouse, sometimes called the long-tailed field mouse (*Apodemus sylvaticus*). It is present in hedgerows as well as woods, gardens and anywhere else it can find food and shelter.

Slightly larger than a house mouse, an adult wood mouse is about 9 cm long from the tip of its pointed nose to the base of its tail; the tail by itself is little short of that length, hence the alternative name for the animal. Its upper parts are an attractive yellow-brown; underneath it is a contrasting white. There is nearly always a spot of buff, yellow or orange on the chest beneath the forelimbs. The large and prominent eyes—adaptations to the wood mouse's nocturnal way of life—and long oval ears, give the animal an air of inquisitive surprise.

Unfortunately, although it is such a charming creature to look at, the wood mouse is not always a friend of the farmer or gardener. This is the delinquent that uses its excellent sense of smell to detect newly

10. Wood mouse (*Apodemus sylvaticus*)

sown peas, grain and other large seeds, and then digs them up and eats them. Other items of food include seedlings, buds, nuts, berries, snails, insects and other small invertebrates. If you care to wait quietly near a hedgerow hazel bush as darkness falls, there is the delightful possibility of seeing a wood mouse scurry up into the slender branches, bite off a nut and chisel at the hard shell with its strong front teeth. The hole the mouse gnaws is slightly irregular and made at the blunt end of the nut. A search of the leaf litter beneath most hazel bushes will soon reveal the evidence of many wood-mouse feasts.

Another sign of wood mice is the presence in the hedgerow of old nests of thrushes and blackbirds filled during the winter with a litter of empty seeds of hips and haws, nibbled acorns and traces of red pulp and droppings. Although the wood mouse does not hibernate, it is a great hoarder and has been known to tuck away, besides fruit and nuts, such varied items as bulbs, birds' eggs, snails and even a lump of putty in one of these feeding places.

Under favourable conditions, wood mice can breed at an alarming rate, there being several litters of between five and nine young during the year. The nest, of dried leaves, mosses and grasses, is in a burrow which the wood mouse digs for itself, although it may also use parts of the disused burrows of other mammals.

There is another, rarer species, similar to the wood mouse, which is occasionally found in hedgerows, although mainly in the south of England. This is the yellow-necked mouse (*Apodemus flavicollis*). It is slightly larger than a wood mouse and instead of a different-coloured spot on its white breast, it has a yellow, orange or buff-coloured band stretching from one foreleg to the other. It is a good idea to examine carefully any wood mice that you may find in case one of them is the much scarcer yellow-necked, a species well worth reporting to your local museum or natural history society.

Voles

Another group of small mammals frequently found in hedgerows is the voles. The most common species are the bank vole (*Clethrionomys glareolus*), and the short-tailed or field vole (*Microtus agrestis*). However, if the hedge is bounded by a water-filled ditch, the larger water vole (*Arvicola amphibius*), or water rat, as it is sometimes inaccurately called, may also be present.

Voles are distinguished by their blunt snouts and short ears, giving the head a rounded appearance rather like that of a small chubby bear. They also have short tails. Both the field vole and the bank vole are about the size of a house mouse. The short-tailed vole has ears that are almost hidden in its greyish-brown fur, and a tail only about one-third of the length of the head and body. The bank vole has longer ears which are nearly always visible above the fur, a somewhat longer tail, about half the length of the body, and reddish or russet-brown fur. Both species are grey, buff or nearly white below.

The short-tailed vole tends to prefer areas of coarse grasses and is, therefore, most often found in hedges which are unkempt or bounded by uncut verges. Its shallow runs and burrows form an elaborate criss-cross system amongst and beneath the grass roots. Here and there in the tunnels are domed chambers or 'parlours' to which, by night and day, the vole conveys little piles of fresh grass stems, cut into convenient lengths, to be eaten there in peace and safety. When the softer grasses are scarce in winter it may turn to bulbs, roots, crops and bark for food.

A brief search of almost any patch of rank grass in or near the hedgerow is almost certain to reveal a short-tailed vole's tunnel; by carefully following and opening this up the whole system can be found. The domed nests of dry grass may be on the ground or in a

11. Short-tailed field vole (*Microtus agrestis*)

Fig. 12 (a) Wood mouse (b) bank vole (c) house mouse (d) common rat

hollow, and here the young are born and nursed. The breeding season extends roughly from March to September, although it sometimes goes on to December. The number of young in a litter varies, but is usually between three and six. Since the young voles are able to breed when they are little more than a month old, the number of these animals can increase rapidly if there is enough food available. Every few years the populations of short-tailed voles gradually build up to a peak, which may occasionally reach plague proportions, and then there is a sudden decline until only a few remain. Being so common, voles, like wood mice, provide an item of food for many predators.

Bank voles prefer hedgerows with undergrowth. They make

shallow burrows and runs, and will form regular highways, both above and below ground, along a hedgebank. Their nests are made of chopped dry grass, sometimes lined with moss, wool or feathers, and usually placed on the ground. Occasionally the nest is built on the foundations of a disused bird's nest, in a tree stump, or underground in a burrow.

Bank voles are good climbers, and better jumpers than their short-tailed relatives. They are also less restricted in their food, eating berries, fruits and some animal material, including insects and their larvae. They will climb bushes and small trees in search of berries or nuts. Hazel nuts are gnawed open, leaving a neat hole surrounded by tooth marks.

Although bank voles may rear four or five litters a year and increase in numbers regularly, they never reach the plague proportions of their short-tailed relatives.

Other hedgerow rodents

Wood mice, yellow-necked mice and voles are all rodents, and have the characteristic pair of sharp, chisel-like incisor teeth at the front of the upper and lower jaws. There is a gap between the incisors and the grinding cheek teeth, which allows these animals to gnaw for long periods without wearing out the cheek teeth.

Another rodent which may be found in hedgerows is the tiny harvest mouse (*Micromys minutus*), one of Britain's smallest mammals. It has a bright chestnut coat, a white belly and a blunter

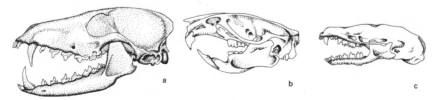

Fig. 13 The skulls and teeth of three mammals
(a) Fox—carnivore (b) Rat—rodent (c) Mole—insectivore

12. Harvest mouse (*Micromys minutus*) using its tail for support

nose than the other mice. It lives mainly in the south and east of England, although there have been a number of records of its being found in Wales, the North and Scotland. Besides hedgerows and grass verges, the harvest mouse is also found in cornfields, dykes, reedbeds, and any area of long grass. It moves gracefully from stalk to stalk, aided by its tail which gives extra support and acts as a fifth limb. Several litters are produced by each pair of harvest mice between April and September. They are born in a nest built of shredded grass blades a few centimetres above the ground in corn, rushes or long grass. In hedgerows and grass verges a favourite nesting place of the harvest mouse seems to be the cocksfoot grass (*Dactylis glomerata*), and a search amongst the tussocks of this grass in winter will frequently reveal the tiny disused spherical breeding nests, little larger than a golf ball. In winter the harvest mouse tunnels into hay or straw stacks, or burrows just below the ground.

Another occasional hedgerow rodent is, perhaps rather surprisingly, the house mouse (*Mus musculus*). This very adaptable little mammal can live almost anywhere, and in country districts it lives in hedgerows, drystone walls and straw during the summer, but after the harvest, house mice invade barns, warehouses and any other places where food can be found.

Although the grey squirrel (*Sciurus carolinensis*) is typically a rodent of woodland, it is sometimes found in hedgerows where numbers of tall trees are present, and also in shelterbelts. This animal, introduced from America in the 1870s, has survived repeated attempts to exterminate it because of the damage it does to trees. Our native red squirrel (*Sciurus vulgaris*) prefers conifer woodland and is most common in Wales, Ireland, the West Country, the northern counties, much of Scotland and the East Anglian Breckland. But in recent years, grey squirrels have moved into Breckland and fewer red squirrels are to be seen.

The grey squirrel is increasing its range, but a mammal which, alas, seems to be decreasing in numbers is the dormouse (*Muscardinus avellanarius*). Even in those few parts of Britain, mainly the south and

13. Grey squirrel (*Sciurus carolinensis*) in characteristic pose

west, where it is found, the dormouse is rarely seen, since it is nocturnal and is unique among our rodents in hibernating during the winter. It lives mainly in woodland, but also in unkempt hedgerows, where it can climb about in the lower branches to find seeds, fruits and insects. Dormice use honeysuckle bark to help build their summer nests, and thus one of the signs of their presence is stripped honeysuckle stems.

The other rodent which unfortunately shows no sign of becoming rare is the brown or common rat (*Rattus norvegicus*). It is common in some hedgerows, particularly in the sugar-beet-growing areas of East Anglia. In the spring it moves into fields, straw stacks, and canal and river banks, as well as hedgerows, from the sewers, stables, outhouses and other buildings where it has spent the winter.

Rabbits

Until the epidemic of the dreadful disease myxomatosis began in 1953, the rabbit (*Oryctolagus cuniculus*), was probably the most common hedgerow mammal. It was introduced into Britain from France in the twelfth century for its meat, and eventually became the most familiar wild mammal of the British countryside as well as one of the most destructive agricultural pests. Incidentally, although the rabbit has many of the features of a rodent, it and the hares are classified into a separate order called the Lagomorpha.

The rabbit is a social animal, living in colonies in warrens. It can thrive in almost any place where it can dig a burrow, and the introduction of hedges and hedgebanks provided it with an ideal place to build its home, surrounded by an abundant supply of food. The burrows damage field boundaries and hedges, and disturb the surrounding soil, encouraging the growth of weeds such as nettles and ragwort (*Senecio jacobaea*).

A pregnant female rabbit, or doe, digs a separate burrow called a stop, which she lines with hay or straw and fur from her own body. Breeding can occur in any month of the year, but mainly between January and June. Although the young rabbits take about nine months to reach adult size, they can breed when they are only three or

14. Rabbit (*Oryctolagus cuniculus*)

four months old. A rabbit rarely lives more than a year and the death rate amongst the young is high since they have many enemies amongst predatory birds and mammals, as well as man.

At dawn and dusk, rabbits emerge from the warren to feed. They use clearly defined runways and their communal latrines are often on a mole-hill. A rabbit will eat 500 g or more of fresh green food in a day. It does much harm to young trees by nibbling the shoots and bark, and also damages pastures, cereals and root crops.

Just as cows, sheep and goats chew the cud to ensure that the cellulose in their food is properly digested, rabbits, and their relatives the hares, have their own special method of feeding, called refection. Food is eaten and then passed out of the body in a semi-digested form as soft moist pellets. These are immediately eaten again and passed through the intestines to be fully digested, leaving the dry pellets that are found on the ground.

Until myxomatosis affected Britain's rabbits, it was estimated that there were over 60 million of them: more than the human population. When the disease struck, the effects on crops and vegetation were soon seen—they grew as never before. Now the disease is no longer as lethal, and the rabbit population seems to increase sporadically until a new outbreak of myxomatosis again reduces its numbers.

Hedgehogs

Another mammal for which the hedge has proved a boon is the hedgehog (*Erinaceus europaeus*). In fact, it gets part of its name from its daytime resting place. Hedgehogs originally lived in open woods, and so hedges must provide an ideal alternative habitat—cover for a nest, and neighbouring fields, parks and gardens in which to search for food.

The hedgehog comes out at night to hunt for food, using its keen senses of smell and hearing. It is most active at dusk and dawn when it

15. Hedgehog (*Erinaceus europaeus*)

feeds mainly on insects and their larvae, slugs, snails, worms and fallen fruit. It will sometimes eat lizards, the eggs and young of ground-nesting birds, and occasionally rats, mice, frogs, and even snakes, including the adder (*Vipera berus*). The hedgehog is immune to the poison given off by the fangs of the adder, and will provoke this snake until it and its poison are exhausted.

Hedgehogs produce one or two litters of between three and seven young, in nests of grass and leaves, from May to September. The nest may be built in the base of a thick hedge, under a tree root or in a disused rabbit burrow. The young are pale, blind and covered with soft whitish spines which, after about eighteen days, begin to harden. The mother suckles the young for a month, after which they start hunting for their own food.

Hedgehogs hibernate between October and early April in nests bigger than those in which they nurse their young and spend the summer. They use leaves and moss to weatherproof the nest and to maintain an even temperature inside. During this time the hedgehog's body temperature sinks from 35°C to just over 4°C, but the animal occasionally wakes up and leaves the nest, even in extreme cold, in the hope of finding food. If there is a hedgehog about at night, one normally has no difficulty in locating it. It advertises itself by the loud rustling it makes amongst the dead leaves and by snuffling and snorting as it searches for slugs and other food. By day the presence of hedgehogs in the neighbourhood is given away by the cylindrical droppings, about 2.5 to 3 cm long, usually black in colour and with pointed ends.

The natural enemies of hedgehogs are foxes and badgers, but the biggest cause of death is the motor car. When a hedgehog hears a vehicle approaching, or any other natural enemy, it curls into a protective ball and remains motionless—hence the frequency with which dead hedgehogs are seen in the roads. If they survive these perils, hedgehogs can live for up to six years.

Moles

Another common hedgerow mammal, which again is not often seen, is the mole *(Talpa europaea)*. In areas which are ploughed and cultivated, hedgerows provide a safe refuge for moles from which they can burrow out into the fields.

Moles live almost entirely under ground, in tunnels which they dig with a breast-stroke action of their short, shovel-shaped front limbs. Tunnelling is carried out from a base, or fortress—a cavity beneath an extra large mole-hill; this is also used for sleeping and breeding. The main reason for the mole's daily tunnelling is to find food—earthworms, insect larvae and slugs.

The mole is well adapted to life underground. As well as its powerful forelimbs for digging, it has a barrel-shaped body covered in soft shiny fur that lies well in any direction. A mole's vision is poor and the minute eyes are hidden beneath fur; the pink nose is pointed and heavily whiskered, and the ears are flapless holes. The senses of touch and hearing are well developed, more than compensating for the poorer ones of sight and smell. The short, stumpy tail is always held erect when the mole is burrowing, enabling it to gauge the size of the tunnel.

The mole is a solitary animal and makes contact with its own kind only when it mates, some time during the period from March to May. The naked, pink young are born between April and June in a nest of grass, dried leaves or moss.

Moles belong to an order of primitive mammals with simple brains called insectivores, and are related to hedgehogs. Most insectivores are very active, and have enormous appetites for their size. The snout of these mammals is long, and they have many teeth which are small and extremely sharp for gripping their wriggling invertebrate food.

Shrews

Other species of insectivore which are commonly found in any hedge with a little ground cover are the common shrew *(Sorex araneus)*, the smaller pygmy shrew *(Sorex minutus)*, and occasionally the water shrew *(Neomys fodiens)*. These restless, hungry mammals have the typical long noses and small sharp teeth. Like the mole they are active throughout the day and night and do not hibernate. Although shrews

16. Mole (*Talpa europaea*)

are so common in hedgerows they are rarely seen. But if you stand quietly by a hedge for a few minutes you can often hear the shrill quarrelsome shrieks emitted when two shrews meet.

The shrew's saliva is poisonous, although it is not powerful enough to do more than cause a burning sensation to the skin of a human who may be bitten. But it will quickly cause death to spiders, earthworms, woodlice and insects of various kinds on which the shrew feeds.

The only animals which regularly eat shrews are owls, stoats and foxes, although a number of other mammals, including cats, frequently kill them. The reason why shrews taste so unpleasant is that they possess scent glands with which they mark their territories and locate each other. They are solitary, aggressive animals, guarding their territories jealously and screaming shrilly at any intruder. If this squeaking contest does not drive the intruder away, a fight may follow, but this does not lead to the death of one of the individuals as often as legend would have us believe.

Mating between shrews takes place between early spring and late summer, and up to five litters of seven or eight young may be born during that period. The breeding nest is a ball of woven grass, placed either below ground or on the surface under cover, in which the mother suckles her young for the first three or four weeks, until they can fend for themselves. As might be expected with animals which reproduce so rapidly, the life span of these restless creatures is short and few live for more than a year.

Carnivores and population control

The population of the mammal species already mentioned in this chapter are controlled partly by birds of prey such as owls and hawks, and also to some extent by the flesh-eating mammals, the carnivores. The latter have large canine or 'dog teeth' with sharp cutting edges that are used for shearing or slicing the flesh which the same sharp incisor teeth have caught. However, it is important to remember that carnivores, like insectivores, do often eat other foods besides flesh and insects respectively.

Foxes and badgers

The two largest British land carnivores, the fox (*Vulpes vulpes*) and the badger (*Meles meles*) will both feed along hedgerows at night. The former eats mainly rabbits, mice, voles, hedgehogs and game birds and occasionally, when food is scarce, insects such as beetles and fruit and berries. The badger's food consists of anything from rabbits, rats, mice, voles, earthworms and wasp larvae to blackberries, bulbs, fungi and green plants. Occasionally a fox will make its 'earth' in a thick hedgerow and, although they are most common in woodland, I have found a number of badger sets in steep hedgebanks adjoining both cultivated and uncultivated fields and also in a hedge adjoining a canal bank in Kent.

Stoats and weasels

The two carnivores most common in hedgerows and most often seen hunting are the stoat (*Mustela erminea*), and the weasel (*Mustela nivalis*). These two carnivores do not get the sympathy they should from farmers and gamekeepers, since both these categories of country-dweller fear an attack on their hen runs or pheasant pens. But stoats and weasels are extremely efficient at keeping the numbers of rabbits, mice, voles, rats and squirrels in check, so reducing the damage these mammals do to farm crops and trees.

Fig. 14 Stoat and weasel

Stoats and weasels are so often confused that it is as well to set out their differences. The stoat is the larger, the more conspicuous and perhaps the better known of the two. An adult male stoat's head and body are about 30 cm long and its tail another 11 to 12 cm. The females are somewhat smaller. Stoats have bushy tails ending in a black tip; they are brown above and white below, but in Scotland and northern England they turn white in winter to match the snows, although this change does not happen in the south. Stoats in this white phase provide the beautiful fur called ermine.

Stoats have only one litter of young a year, in the spring, but these are produced as a result of mating the previous summer. The youngsters, five to eight in number, follow their mother to learn how to hunt, forming family parties that last well into autumn.

The male weasel is much smaller than the stoat, about 26 cm long, including a 6 cm tail which tapers and has no black tip. Again, the female is smaller than the male, but white forms in winter are very rare in Britain. There are normally two litters a year of about six young, which are born approximately six weeks after mating.

Stoats and weasels differ somewhat in their feeding habits and hunting grounds, although no sharp line can be drawn. The stoat will venture out into the open to pursue game birds and rabbits, and will occasionally climb trees. Rabbits appear to be petrified by stoats and lie down and scream just before the kill, which the stoat administers with a bite of its needle-sharp teeth behind the victim's neck. It does not appear to occur to the hapless rabbit to make a break for open country, where it could elude the stoat with its greater speed; instead the rabbit falls, panic-stricken, long before it is exhausted. Nor does it seem to occur to other rabbits to come to the aid of the victim.

One can also occasionally see a stoat lure its prey by another unusual method. The animal jumps, twists, chases its tail and performs somersaults. Soon a group of small birds flutters around the stoat, chattering noisily at it. They 'mob' it to show their lack of fear and to reveal the stoat's dangerous presence to their fellows. This goes on harmlessly for some minutes, and then the stoat takes a higher jump than usual, falling with an unfortunate small bird between its paws. It is difficult to understand how the stoat learnt to fool them so.

By contrast, the weasel is more of a mouser, although it will occasionally take a young rabbit. It explores runs and burrows, ferreting through the long grass for mice and voles, or working along the tangled branches of hedgerows in search of eggs and nestlings. So far as is known, the weasel does not appear to have developed the unusual forms of hunting behaviour described for the stoat.

The interrelationships of herbivores and carnivores

The carnivores or predators such as the stoat, weasel, fox and badger, as well as the birds of prey, could not exist without the herbivores or plant-eating animals, which in turn could not live without green plants. But do the plant-eaters gain any benefit from being eaten? The answer to this strange question seems to be that they do benefit to some extent. Some of the plagues of short-tailed voles reported in the past, when thousands of voles starved to death or damaged crops and trees, may have been due to the widespread destruction of predators by gamekeepers. The introduced grey squirrel would not have become a pest if its natural enemies were also present in this country. The one mammal which could chase, catch and kill squirrels in their tree-top homes is the pine marten (*Martes martes*). And this beautiful relative of the weasel has become one of Britain's rarest mammals because of persecution by man. Similarly the original important enemies of our wild deer have been exterminated, so that now the numbers have to be kept under control by experts armed with powerful rifles, if the deer are not to starve, become diseased or cause great damage.

Studying hedgerow mammals

Studying our hedgerow mammals is not easy. If you have the time, and patience, one of the most rewarding ways to see hedgerow mammals and other animals in action is simply to sit quietly, with binoculars if you have them, and watch and wait. Sooner or later something of interest will happen.

Another method, with a higher success rate for less time, is to put down bait for the hedgerow mammals. This is best done during the autumn and winter when there are fewer leaves about to obscure your vision.

Obtain some scrap fat from the butcher and melt this down in a saucepan. Add any spare bacon rinds, some crumbs of bread and perhaps a few sunflower seeds, and let the mixture set. Scoop out a larger chunk every evening and leave it by the hedgerow, in the same place each time. You can see by the toothmarks in the fat each morning whether it is being eaten. When animals seem to be feeding on the bait nightly, go out and sit very quietly about two metres down-wind from the bait. A hide is not necessary, but warm, dark clothing is a 'must'. A small folding stool will more than repay in comfort its cost to you.

The eyes of nocturnal mammals are not sensitive to red light, so that if you cover the glass of your torch with a piece of red cellophane you can use the torch without fear of disturbing the animals you are watching. The red cellophane reduces the range of the torch's beam, so a fairly powerful torch is advisable. House mice and wood mice are the likeliest visitors, but if you are lucky you may also see shrews, hedgehogs and moles.

The same kind of procedure can be followed for watching rabbits, although the bait should be bran, lettuce or cabbage, and the distance at which you sit from the bait must be much greater. Fortunately rabbits are most active at dusk and dawn, so that a torch is not really necessary.

If your hedge has a water-filled ditch where water voles live, these can be baited with small pieces of apple or apple-peelings, and watched, if you keep still and wear dark clothing, in *daylight*.

There is still a great deal to be learned about the lives of our wild mammals, and careful recording of your observations can tell us a great many new facts about their behaviour.

5·Amphibians and Reptiles

If the British Isles are poor in mammal species, there are even fewer amphibians and reptiles. And hedges, or rather hedgebanks and ditches, are important habitats for the few species we have.

Frogs, toads and newts are classified as amphibians. The name refers to their ability to live both on land and in fresh water. However, the amphibians can never be completely independent of water, for their thin moist skins are liable to dry out quite quickly when they are not in a damp place, and in any case they have to return to the water to lay their eggs. Also, like the fish and reptiles, amphibians cannot regulate their body temperature, so they need to be warmed before they can become active, and in the winter they must hibernate to avoid being frozen to death. All the British amphibians are able to hibernate on land, although the frogs and newts do spend the winter in the mud under water on occasion.

In view of the amphibians' need for warm, moist conditions and their diet of insects and other invertebrates, it is perhaps not surprising that hedges, and especially those hedges running parallel to a water-filled ditch, are very suitable places to find them. But again, as we have already found with mammals, amphibians are rarely seen, because they remain under cover and are most active on mild, damp nights.

Toads

The amphibian which is probably seen most often in hedgerows is the common toad (*Bufo bufo*). There are two species of toad native to

Britain. The common toad is easily distinguished from a frog by its dry, warty skin, flat back, shorter limbs and slow clumsy gait. The other species, the natterjack (*Bufo calamita*), is smaller, with a maximum length of about 6.5 cm. It moves by running 'like a mouse' and may be recognised at once by the yellow line along the middle of the head and back. It is much rarer in most areas than the common toad.

By day toads live in holes—either natural ones beneath tree roots, or holes which they or burrowing mammals have scraped in the earth. At dusk they leave their holes to search for worms, snails, woodlice, caterpillars, beetles and other insects. A toad feeds voraciously, catching its prey with its tongue. The tongue of a toad, unlike that of a human, is hinged to the floor of the mouth by its front end. When a suitable invertebrate animal comes near, the free end of the sticky tongue lashes out and the prey is caught. The toad does not use its forefeet to hold a wriggling creature as you might expect; instead the victim is wedged in the toad's jaw by squashing it with the eyeballs, which can be pulled right down into the mouth cavity.

Toads hibernate in October and November, choosing disused mammal burrows, particularly those protected by trees. The toads emerge from hibernation in March or April and return to the stretch of water where they were born. This may be a pond, canal, slow-flowing stream or deep ditch, and the same stretch of water is, in many cases, returned to year after year. Sometimes the toads from over a considerable area arrive within a few hours of each other. Often when such large groups of toads have to cross roads many are killed by passing traffic.

When they have reached the breeding ground the male toads wait around for a female to appear. They are not always content to sit idly; sometimes they poise themselves half in and half out of the water and begin to announce their presence to any female who takes notice of their loud rattling croaks.

The toads pair up, the male clinging to the female's back, and the female lays her spawn in a string 2 to 7 metres long, containing as many as 7000 black eggs. These develop into small tadpoles that go through similar stages to those of the frog, finally becoming small tail-less toads. At first the young toads remain near their birth-place, sheltering during strong sunshine. A fall of rain, particularly if it is preceded by drought, will sometimes bring many thousands of young toads out of hiding. These large collections, appearing after rain, gave rise to the old belief that it sometimes 'rained' toads. Again, as they disperse, many have to cross roads and are killed by passing traffic.

A large proportion of young toads fail to reach maturity, for they also have many natural enemies. Crows and birds of prey, rats, stoats, hedgehogs and grass snakes will eat them, but the toad is not entirely defenceless.

A frightened toad 'freezes' to the ground, where it is camouflaged by its earthy-looking skin. It is also able to change the shade of its skin to a small extent. The toad fills its lungs with air and blows out its body so that it may look half as big again. The sight of such a large bulbous toad often deters enemies, including many snakes, which would be unable to swallow so large a bulk.

If these measures fail, the toad's second line of defence comes into action. The pimples on the toad's skin are really glands, and they produce an evil-tasting milky liquid. A dog which has the misfortune to pick up a toad hastily drops it. It would be unlikely to tackle another toad for a long time. The liquid given off by the toad's skin is not, however, poisonous to the human skin and it does not produce warts, as is often believed.

The swelling up of its body by a frightened toad seems to be an instinctive reaction to any snake-like object. You can easily demonstrate it by slowly waving a piece of rubber tubing over a toad. I have seen the same result produced by a handful of wriggling worms. Experiment with different lengths and thicknesses of tubing, and try to find the smallest 'snake' that will bring about the 'freezing' reaction.

Frogs

Frogs are also often found in hedgerows, particularly the immature frogs, which usually hibernate away from water in any convenient hole. By contrast, many adult common frogs (*Rana temporaria*) creep

17. Common frog (*Rana temporaria*)

into ready-made holes in the soft mud at the bottom of a ditch or pond to hibernate under water, but some spend the winter on land.

The common frog varies greatly in colour and it is capable of changing its background colour slowly to match its surroundings. But it always has dark cross-bars on its limbs and a dark patch which covers the region of the eardrum behind the eye. Two other species of frog are found in the British Isles, the marsh frog (*Rana ridibunda*), and the edible frog (*R. esculenta*), but both are introduced species which have very limited distribution in Britain.

The breeding habits of frogs are basically the same as those of toads, except that frogs lay their eggs in a mass of spawn, unlike the long strings of eggs produced by toads. The frog also catches its food in a similar way to the toad—insects are caught with a rapid flick of the tongue.

Newts

The three closely related species of newts found in the British Isles can be mistaken for lizards, except that lizards, being reptiles, have scaly skins, whereas newts have smooth skins that are sometimes covered with lumps or warts.

Of the three newt species, the smooth (*Triturus vulgaris*), palmate (*T. helveticus*) and great crested or warty (*T. cristatus*), the smooth newt is the most common, and also the one most likely to be seen in hedgerows. It grows up to 10 cm long and has a spotted throat. The male smooth newt has a wavy crest and is brown to olive-brown in

Fig. 15 The three British species of newt (a) Smooth newt (*Triturus vulgaris*) (b) Palmate newt (*T. helveticus*) (c) Great crested or warty newt (*T. cristatus*)

colour, marked with darker spots. Its underside is yellow to rose coloured, and there is a middle area coloured red with black spots. Females do not have a crest and are paler yellow brown.

In early spring newts enter the water to breed. The females lay 200 to 300 eggs singly on water plants, each enclosed in a protective coat of jelly. Like those of frogs and toads, the newt eggs hatch into a larval stage, similar to a tadpole, which has gills. In ten weeks lungs and legs have grown and the gills are lost. The young newt then leaves the water, to which it may not return again until it is two or three years old.

Adult newts also leave the water at the end of the breeding season and spend the rest of the year on land, hidden in damp places. They emerge at night to feed on slugs, earthworms and other small invertebrates.

Common lizards

The reptile most often found in Britain, the common lizard (*Lacerta vivipara*), is quite frequent in hedgerows but is rarely noticed since its brown body, mottled with black, blends so well with the abundant cover. It lives in loose colonies and enjoys basking on the warm surfaces of stone, moss or bark. When disturbed it will dart into hiding, but once quiet returns it is quick to reappear.

The common lizard feeds wholly on insects and other small invertebrates, especially grasshoppers and spiders. As the Latin name *vivipara* suggests, the female bears her young alive; they hatch from eggs retained inside the body until just before their birth in midsummer. They are tiny and fragile, only 2.5 cm long, and for the first year or so have to seek the smallest of invertebrate prey, until they reach the adult size of about 15 cm, half of which consists of the tail.

Lizards hibernate all through the winter, and even in summer are really active only in warm sunshine. Their long, slender tails readily snap off if seized. A new tail eventually grows, but is more stumpy than the original.

18. Common lizard (*Lacerta vivipara*)

Slow worms

Another lizard which is often found in dampish places along hedgerows is the slow worm or blind worm (*Anguis fragilis*). In actual fact this reptile is neither blind nor a worm. It is a lizard which has no legs and hence is also often mistaken for a snake, although unlike a snake's its eyes have movable lids.

You may recognise the slow worm by its uniform greyish-brown colour and smooth skin. The females may have a dark stripe along the back. Occasionally some slow worms develop blue spots as they mature. If you pick up a slow worm it will thrust out its forked tongue from its small mouth. The slow worm lives on slugs, earthworms, and insects and their larvae. It is wholly beneficial to farmers and gardeners, and it is a pity that it suffers so often for its snake-like appearance.

Like other lizards, a slow worm picked up by its tail will promptly snap off that organ, leaving it wriggling in your hand. This escape device baffles its enemies and the slow worm itself is unhurt by the loss of its tail, which eventually regrows, although it is never as long or slender as before.

When they hibernate in winter, slow worms creep away into some hole or heap of leaves; rotting timber or crevices in old tree-trunks are also often selected as sleeping places. Slow worms mate in spring, and the females retain the soft eggs within the body until late summer, laying them only when the young slow worms are just about to emerge from their shells. These tiny young, up to twenty in number, are silver in colour with a dark line on their backs. They take several years to reach breeding size and may ultimately grow to a length of about 45 cm.

Adders

Two of Britain's three species of snake are also often found in hedgerows. The adder or viper (*Vipera berus*), is the commonest snake in hedgerows as well as woodlands and heaths. It is found all over Britain, though not in Ireland, but in some districts it is quite

grass snake

adder

Fig. 16 Adder and grass snake

scarce and in others remarkably abundant. The adder likes dry, well-drained places, hence the attraction of hedgebanks. It is our only poisonous reptile, and has two very effective hollow fangs, through which it discharges its venom from special glands into the bloodstream of its victim. The adder regularly uses its poison to paralyse small creatures, such as mice, voles, shrews, lizards and slow worms, so that having once struck it can eat them at leisure. A large meal can last the snake for a week.

Even where adders are common the risk from them is not great. An adder will never attack a human unless it is suddenly disturbed. Normally the snake slinks off unseen. However, anyone who is bitten should be kept quiet, reassured and taken to the nearest doctor or hospital.

The adder is quite easy to recognise because it bears a dark zigzag line running down its back from neck to tail, while on its head there is a forward-pointing V-mark, easily remembered as 'V for viper'. The body colour below the dark zigzag line is curiously variable. Adders may be reddish, brownish, greyish, yellowish or whitish. Females are duller and longer than the males, being about 60 cm long, but both male and female adders are noticeably stouter than other snakes.

With the first frosts, adders hibernate by retiring into a ready-made burrow. On rare occasions groups of hibernating adders have been found. When they awake in spring, the adults pair. The female produces eggs but retains them within her body for nearly four months, only laying them when they are about to hatch into babies, already some 16 cm long. Almost immediately the young snakes strike out on their own, knowing instinctively how to hunt their prey.

Grass snakes

Harmless to humans, though often killed out of hand by those who distrust all snakes or snake-like creatures, is the grass snake (*Natrix natrix*). But for those able to control their destructive urges long enough, the differences between it and the adder are readily apparent. The grass snake lacks completely the zigzag line down the back, nor does it bear the V-mark. The two pale yellow or orange patches on the back of the neck, with two black triangles behind, are good clues to look for. The body colour can vary widely—olive-greens or olive-browns are common, but grass snakes may also be greyish, brownish or yellowish, with black vertical bars on the sides and two rows of smaller spots on the back. They hibernate in the winter, sometimes in groups, and pair in the spring. About midsummer the females lay strings of about twenty or thirty white eggs, which look like birds' eggs except that their skins are soft like parchment. These eggs, however, are seldom seen, being laid as a rule in drifts of decaying leaves which, by their fermentation, supplement the heat of the sun. The mother snake may sometimes guard her eggs, but she does not incubate them, nor does she look after her young.

Six to ten weeks after the eggs are laid, the little snakes break out and wander off in search of food. They are then about 16 to 19 cm long, and are able to pursue and swallow only the smallest of prey— worms, grubs and soft-bodied insects. Gradually they grow to a considerable size, the females reaching an average of 90 cm, the males 60 cm; they become more active and are able to tackle larger victims. They seem to prefer frogs, but take a variety of animal food, including tadpoles, fish, newts, eggs, and nestling field voles. Lacking poisonous fangs, grass snakes swallow their prey whole, raking it down with their backward-pointing teeth until it dies from suffocation.

If a grass snake is caught and handled, its first reaction is to void a mass of foul-smelling excrement, and to struggle violently to escape. Occasionally a captured grass snake will turn over on its back, and lie with belly upturned, mouth open and tongue hanging out, shamming death. Nevertheless a grass snake is readily tamed and will become quite a docile pet, easy to handle. However, it is difficult to feed, because of its insistence on small living animals, and is far better left where you found it.

Grass snakes are amazingly agile swimmers, and take much of their prey in the water. They can also climb trees readily and may take young birds as well as eggs from their nests. But they never wander far from moist areas, such as the banks of ditches, streams and rivers, marshes and damp woodland. Here the grass snake's behaviour contrasts with that of the adder, which loves dry sunny spots.

The effects of hedgerow removal on Britain's amphibians and reptiles

Britain's amphibians and reptiles have already suffered greatly from such factors as over-collecting, pollution by pesticides and other agricultural chemicals, the draining or destruction of ponds, streams, ditches and other wet areas, and the ploughing and burning of heathland.

Hedges, banks and ditches are prime habitats for the few species of amphibians and reptiles we have, as well as providing important migration routes for them. If we allow too many more hedges to be lost, then there is a very real threat of extinction to these most interesting and beneficial creatures.

6·Invertebrates in Hedgerows

Amongst the invertebrates is a fascinating world of small animals awaiting discovery by the interested and intelligent young naturalist. Many of these creatures, particularly snails, slugs, woodlice, millipedes, centipedes, harvestmen, spiders, plant bugs and bush crickets, have been rather neglected as subjects for study by field biologists.

Collecting hedgerow invertebrates

Almost any country hedgerow, especially one on a grassy bank, is a good place to begin a search. A few screw-top jars or smaller glass or plastic collecting-tubes are all you need, together with a pair of sharp eyes, aided perhaps by a hand lens. If you can also visit the hedgerow by night with a torch, you will not be disappointed. Many of these small nocturnal invertebrates are difficult to find by day, since they are so well hidden in the soil, deeply buried in leaf litter, under stones and such places. Others have cryptic coloration, either being similar in colour to their background, or making use of elaborate camouflage, patterning and structure to help them remain hidden.

The food of hedgerow invertebrates

Many invertebrates feed on the young leaves of hedgerow plants. When these leaves fall in the late summer and autumn, they provide food for the vast numbers of invertebrates that live on the leaf litter that collects at the hedge bottom. Other invertebrates feed on fungi and lichens on old and decaying stems; some eat fruits at different stages of their development. Many feed on the nectar and pollen of hedgerow flowers while some, which may spend the summer in crops, roadside verges or grassland, pass the winter in hedgerows, hibernating under bark or in the leaf-litter layer. All these invertebrates, however or wherever they live in the hedgerow, have a wide range of parasites and predators associated with them. Some of the predators are the animals we met in the last three chapters, but many are themselves invertebrates.

There is not the space available here to describe the hundreds of species which may be found in a few metres of hedgerow. In any case, many of these are small and inconspicuous and have no common name. Instead we will examine a representative sample of the most abundant animals, particularly those which feed on living leaves or fruits of some of the more common hedgerow plants. As we have already said, no other habitat, except the margins of deciduous woodland, is so rich in shrub species as a hedge. And since most of these shrub species are associated with special forms of invertebrate life, a hedge is clearly a first-class place to study the relationships between animals and plants.

Insect inhabitants of hedgerow hawthorns

Because it is so common and widespread and has palatable leaves, hawthorn is the food of many insects. The caterpillars of eighty species of the larger moths, for instance, eat it. Fortunately for the hawthorn, most of these caterpillars eat other plants as well, so that hawthorn bushes are seldom stripped of all their leaves. On the few occasions this does happen, the caterpillars of the winter moth (*Operophtera brumata*), and mottled umber moth (*Erannis defoliaria*) are the chief culprits.

The winter moth is one of the most common moths in the British Isles. As its name implies, it is on the wing in the early winter when other species are hibernating. Its green looper caterpillars—so called because of the way they move—can be found in May and June on almost any deciduous tree, but especially hawthorn, oak and fruit trees. The number of caterpillars depends on how well the hatching out of the eggs coincides with the appearance of young leaves. If the caterpillars hatch too early, they cannot find leaves on which to feed, while those which hatch late find the leaves too tough for them to eat.

In years when there is a big population of caterpillars, there is a high death-rate in the chrysalis stage. This is probably because ground beetles eat the chrysalids formed when the caterpillars have descended from the trees and burrowed into the soil to pupate. The moths hatch out in October or November and crawl back up the tree-trunks. The females are wingless and look like spiders, whereas the males are thin-bodied, brownish-grey in colour, with a wing-span of about 2.5 cm.

Winter moths hide away during the day, but the males are easy to see at night. They settle on tree-trunks or fly lazily until they find one of the females. The latter are well camouflaged and difficult to see. The best way to find one is to look for a male that is on a tree-trunk facing downwards. It will almost certainly be mating and a closer examination of the tree-trunk will reveal the female. After mating the female walks up a branch to lay her eggs.

The mottled umber moth also has spider-like wingless females and it too is active during the winter months.

Another interesting moth whose caterpillars feed on hawthorn

Fig. 17 Winter and mottled umber moths
(a) Male and female winter moth (*Operophtera brumata*)
(b) male and female mottled umber moth (*Erannis defoliaria*)

leaves, and also the leaves of another common hedgerow shrub, the blackthorn or sloe, is the Chinese character (*Cilix glaucata*). Although this moth is mainly white in colour, it can sit boldly on the leaves of hedgerow shrubs during the summer months, because its shape and pattern disguise it as a bird-dropping. Another white moth, the yellow-tail (*Euproctis similis*), lays its eggs on the tip of a hawthorn leaf and then covers them with a bunch of hairs off the end of its body. The caterpillars that hatch from the eggs are evidently distasteful to birds, since they are brightly coloured with red hair-tufts and feed conspicuously out in the open. The chrysalids are also covered with irritating hairs, so this insect is well protected at all stages.

Another interesting hawthorn moth is the small lackey (*Malacosoma neustria*). It flies by night in July and August throughout England and Wales, as far north as Lancashire and Yorkshire. On rare occasions it also occurs in Scotland and Northern Ireland. Like their relatives, the other eggar moths, many of which are also common in hedgerows, adult lackeys have no proper mouth—this is unnecessary since the moths do not feed during their short active life of only one to three weeks. The red-, white- and blue-striped caterpillars hatch from overwintered eggs and live in crowds on webs slung conspicuously across the branches of hawthorn and blackthorn bushes.

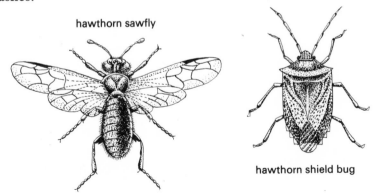

hawthorn sawfly

hawthorn shield bug

Fig. 18 Hawthorn sawfly (*Trichosoma tibiale*) and hawthorn shield bug (*Acanthosoma haemorrhodale*)

Among other moth caterpillars which feed on hawthorn leaves are the magpie (*Abraxus grossulariata*), figure of eight (*Diloba coeruleocephala*), early thorn (*Selenia bilunaria*), scalloped oak (*Crocallis elinguaria*), swallow-tailed (*Ourapteryx sambucaria*), brimstone (*Opisthograptis luteolata*), vapourer (*Orgyia antiqua*), and several emerald moths, including the light emerald (*Campaea margaritata*).

The pale green larvae of one of our biggest sawflies, the hawthorn sawfly (*Trichosoma tibiale*), feed on the leaves of hawthorn from July to September. They spend the winter in brown oblong cocoons, about 2 cm long, which are attached to hawthorn twigs. From these cocoons, the adult sawfly, whose wings are 3 cm across, emerges during May by neatly cutting the cap of the cocoon.

Hawthorn berries provide food for another insect which is very common everywhere except in Scotland. This is the red and green hawthorn shield bug (*Acanthosoma haemorrhodale*), one of our biggest bugs, with a length of 14 mm. It is commonly found hiding among the leaves of hawthorn and blackthorn, and when haws are not about this insect will feed on oak leaves. Shield bugs are so named because of their flat, broad bodies, which are shaped like heraldic shields. They pierce their food with their beak-like mouthparts.

Hedgerow butterflies

Only a few species of butterfly caterpillars feed on hedgerow bushes. Probably the most conspicuous of these butterflies is the brimstone (*Gonepteryx rhamni*), which has the distinction of being one of the first insects likely to be met by the rambler in the early part of the year. This beautiful yellow creature (the female is yellowish-green) is often awakened from hibernation by the first warm sun, sometimes even in January. It is the only British butterfly which hibernates in the open, choosing a thick evergreen bush to shelter it from the rigours of winter. The eggs are laid in May or June under the leaves of buckthorn shrubs, and the caterpillars which emerge are green when mature, merging into bluish-green on the sides, with shining black specks. There is a pale line along each side of the caterpillar. It feeds in June and July and then forms a bluish-green chrysalis from which

19. Brimstone butterfly (*Gonepteryx rhamni*) feeding on the flowers of red clover (*Trifolium pratense*)

the perfect insect emerges at the end of July or the beginning of August.

Some other butterflies associated with hedgerow shrubs and trees include the black-veined white (*Aporia crataegi*), whose caterpillars can be found on blackthorn and hawthorn, and the brown hairstreak (*Zephyrus betulae*), which also lays its eggs on the projecting young shoots of hawthorn. Unfortunately, it has been found that about 80 per cent of the brown hairstreak eggs are lost when a hedge is trimmed.

If there are only a few species of butterfly caterpillars to be found on hedgerow shrubs, there are many on the plants beneath hedges. The gatekeeper (*Epinephele tithonus*), wall (*Pararge megaera*), and other brown butterflies lay their eggs on various species of grasses, the caterpillars of the comma (*Polygonia c-album*), small tortoiseshell (*Aglais urticae*), and peacock butterflies (*Nymphalis io*), feed on the leaves of stinging nettle (*Urtica dioica*), the orange-tip (*Anthocharis cardamines*) and green-veined white butterfly (*Pieris napi*) caterpillars feed on the leaves of Jack-by-the-hedge or garlic mustard (*Alliaria petiolata*), a common hedgerow plant. The caterpillars of

20. Peacock butterfly (*Nymphalis io*) showing the distinctive 'eye spot' on each wing

the beautiful fritillary butterflies (*Argynnis* spp.) eat the leaves of the common dog violet (*Viola riviniana*) and related plants. These are some of the many beautiful and harmless insects which lose their habitat when a hedgerow is uprooted.

Invertebrate visitors to blackberries

Another hedgerow plant which supports a multitude of animal species is the blackberry or bramble (*Rubus fruticosus*). Throughout the year a study of a clump of blackberry bushes will reveal many of the intricate ways in which the lives of animals are linked together in what is often called a *food web*. A good point to start is with the blackberry fruits as they ripen in autumn, but any time of the year will do.

Insects abound near the ripe blackberry fruits and a closer examination will soon reveal that they have different behaviour patterns. Some bask on the leaves, while others, such as the hoverflies (*Syrphidae*) never seem to alight at all. Of those which do alight on the fruits, some of the most common and the biggest nuisance to the blackberry picker, are the wasps (*Vespa* spp.), which often have their nests in hedgebanks. The wasps use their complicated biting mouthparts to tear open the skin on the succulent blackberries to get at the juicy flesh. Once the wasps have damaged the fruit sufficiently for the juices to ooze out, multitudes of tiny yellowish flies, relatives of the vinegar fly (*Drosophila* sp.), which is often used by geneticists in their studies of inheritance, alight. These feed in a different way from the wasps. They force saliva down their proboscis and then suck up the partially digested juice using the proboscis like a drinking straw. In wooded areas, a speckled wood butterfly (*Pararge egeria*) may also use its proboscis to obtain blackberry juices, while another common butterfly feeder on the juice of mushy blackberries is the red admiral (*Vanessa atalanta*).

In bright sunshine, green-bottle flies (*Lucilia caesar*), bluebottles (*Calliphora* spp.), and drone flies (*Eristalis tenax*) settle on the blackberry fruits to feed. Other common visitors are ichneumon wasps (*Ichneumon* spp.), which are attracted, not by the blackberries,

21. Red admiral butterfly (*Vanessa atalanta*) feeding on the flowers of lesser burdock (*Arctium minus*)

but by the larvae of flies, moths and beetles that have hatched from
eggs originally laid in the blackberry flower-heads. The parasitic
ichneumon wasps lay their eggs inside living hosts such as the larvae
of insects, including butterflies, as well as those already mentioned.

During the night the feast on the blackberries does not stop. At
times almost every ripe fruit has one or more earwigs (*Forficula
auricularia*) sitting on it. Earwigs are supposed to use their wings
rarely; whether they reach the fruits by climbing or flying is not clear.
Many night-flying moths, including some of the large hawk moths,
may also stop to feast on the blackberry juices.

And by night and by day, huge armies of spiders hang motionless
in or near their webs, waiting for unsuspecting insect visitors to the

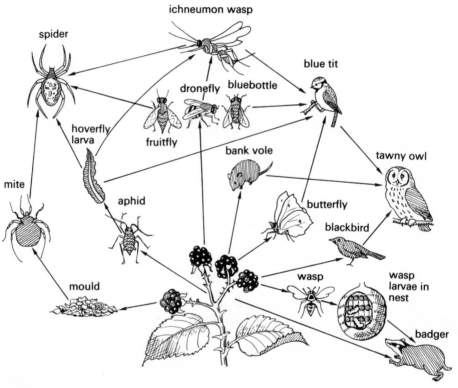

Fig. 19 Food web of a blackberry bush

22. Flowering head of hogweed (*Heracleum sphondylium*)

blackberry plant to blunder into their delicate but efficient traps. The common garden or orb spider (*Araneus diadematus*) sits in the centre of its web, waiting for an insect to get caught in the sticky drops on the spiral thread. The common species of money spider (*Linyphiidae*) hang beneath their hammock webs, ready to dart at any small insect that gets trapped by the scaffolding and falls on to the web. However caught, the victims are stabbed by the fangs of the spiders, which inject poison. Often the spiders then wrap their prey in silk and carry it to their nests.

Even the blackberries that have gone mouldy have their own food links, for the fungus provides food for yet another population of small animals, relatives of the spiders, the mites (*Acari*).

And of course, as mentioned in Chapter 3, blackberries attract many species of birds, and mammals such as the wood mouse, bank vole, and even the badger. These birds and mammals pass out the undigested blackberry seeds in their droppings, ensuring that blackberry plants grow in new, widely scattered habitats.

Some more hedgerow plants to study

I have spent quite a lot of time examining some of the invertebrate visitors to blackberry fruits, but the blackberry flowers and those of a number of other hedgerow plants are equally worthy of study. These include the hogweed (*Heracleum sphondylium*), when it is in flower from June to September. The hollow dead stems of this plant are also worth examining in the autumn and winter for hibernating invertebrates. Ivy (*Hedera helix*) is another good subject for investigation. It not only frequently provides cover for resting animals, including birds, under its shiny evergreen leaves, but its greenish-yellow flowers, which are produced in October, attract numerous insects, and its purplish-black berries, which ripen in early spring, are taken by many birds.

Parasitic invertebrates living on hedgerow plants

Mention was made earlier of a parasitic animal, the ichneumon wasp, living off another animal, but there are many other animals which live as parasites on hedgerow plants.

Almost any blackberry bush will, if searched, be found to have some of its leaves marked with twisty, whitish lines that taper from one end to the other. These are the work of the caterpillars of a tiny moth, the blackberry leaf miner (*Nepticula aurella*), and the marks on the leaf show where the animal has devoured tissues from within the leaf. The actual moth has golden-brown wings passing to violet at the tips, with an oblique pale golden band.

Some larvae eat patches of tissue, which show up as blotches on the surface of the leaf, rather than a continuous winding tunnel. A typical blotch-miner is the caterpillar of the moth *Lithocolletis coryli*, which feeds on the leaves of hazel, but there are many other species to be found on a variety of hedgerow plants. In general, each species usually confines itself to a single kind of plant and to making a particular type of mine. Not all mines are caused by moths, though;

some are made by weevils, sawflies and two-winged flies.

Few naturalists concern themselves with the little insects whose larvae produce leaf-mines, but it is well worth breeding a few of them just to examine their delicate beauty with a hand lens and then release them.

When you have found a leaf that has been mined, hold it up to the light to see if larvae are still present. Obtain an ordinary plant pot and half fill it with clean moist sand. Put the leaf on the sand, and lay a sheet of glass or polythene over the top of the pot. Keep the pot in a warm place out of direct sunshine. If condensation forms on the underside of the glass or polythene, turn the cover over and the water will dry up. Do this every morning until the condensation stops. Correct maintenance of humidity is very important in breeding these creatures. When the little insects emerge, they will usually be found sitting on the underside of the glass or polythene.

Many plants in the hedgerow will show the results of the attacks of other parasitic animals, but these plants react to the injury by growing. The *gall* which develops may look very different from the

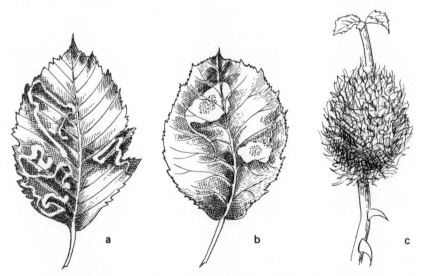

Fig. 20 (a) Blackberry leaf miner (*Nepticula aurella*) (b) hazel blotch mine (*Lithocolletis coryli*) (c) Robin's pincushion (*Diplolepis rosae*)

organ which produced it, but every gall grows entirely from the plant's own tissues.

The gall is of benefit to the creature which causes it, since it provides both shelter and a supply of food. Probably most plants can produce galls, but they do so only if they are damaged by the right parasite. This is an insect in most cases, such as a fly, wasp, bug, midge, beetle, or moth caterpillar. But mites, eelworms, fungi and bacteria can also cause galls.

If there is an oak tree in the hedge, this is almost certain to have a number of different types of galls on it. These are dealt with very fully in another book in this series (*The World of a Tree*). However, one of the most conspicuous of hedgerow galls is the fuzzy green or red gall several centimetres across which is often found on wild rose shoots. It is usually called a robin's pincushion and is caused by a gall wasp (*Diplolepis rosae*) which lays her eggs in spring in leaf buds of the rose. The eggs hatch into larvae and as the larvae grow so does the gall tissue around them. Sometimes neighbouring galls may fuse together.

Although the gall has a firm core it is completely covered with a mossy-looking outer layer of branched filaments that look like thousands of slender pins stuck in a pincushion—hence the name. As the gall grows it is also frequently invaded by the gall wasp's insect enemies as well as quite a crowd of harmless lodgers. In an examination of 800 of these galls, an entomologist found a total of 24,000 insects, of which only a third belonged to the species of wasp which originally caused the gall.

Invertebrates of the herb layer

A good method of collecting the insects and other invertebrates living in the plant life at the foot of the hedge or along the grass verge, is to use a technique called sweeping. The sweep net consists of a strong wire frame to which is attached a bag of strong, closely-woven material such as calico. The depth of the net or its colour does not matter, nor is it important whether the net is triangular or round, although the former is easier to use. The net is swept through the herbage close to the ground and examined every little while. If you can, try to identify the various animals in your catch and rear some of them. But do not take any more of a species than you want for further investigation. Release the others where you caught them.

As well as the myriads of grass-sucking bugs and aphids and countless small spiders, your catch may well contain a number of beetles, of which 3,700 species live in the British Isles. This total includes several hundred species of ground beetle, the most common being the violet ground beetle (*Carabus violaceus*), which gets its name from the violet sheen of its wing cases. Most ground beetles are black, but green and copper sheens are also common.

Few ground beetles can fly, but all are predators. Both larvae and adults hide in crevices by day, coming out at night to feed. They rely on powerful jaws and long legs to prey on worms, caterpillars and small invertebrates.

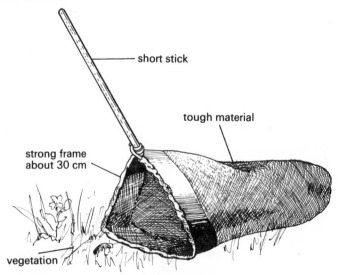

short stick

tough material

strong frame
about 30 cm

vegetation

Fig. 21 Using a sweep net

Inhabitants of hedgerow leaf litter

If the number of invertebrates in the plant life of the hedgerow is large, the number of these animals to be found in the leaf-litter layer on the ground is immense. Many of these animals are springtails (*Collembola*); there are more than 300 species in Britain. They owe their name to a special forked spring at the hind end of their body. The spring is usually bent forwards and held on the underside of the body by a knob, which acts as a catch. When this knob is contracted, the spring is released, propelling the tiny insect forwards, sometimes 30 cm or more.

By searching through the leaf litter you will also find earthworms, mites, ants, woodlice, centipedes, millipedes, many more beetles in all stages of development, moth pupae, and lots of other small animals.

Fig. 22 Springtail from above, and jumping

Hedgerow molluscs

If it has been raining before a visit to a hedgerow you will probably encounter several species of snails and slugs amid the herbage or crawling over the leaf litter. If not, a search under large stones or rotting wood will probably reveal several species of these molluscs, including the grey field slug (*Agriolimax reticulatus*), and the large black and red slugs (*Arion ater*). There will probably also be specimens of the grove or brown-lipped snail (*Cepaea nemoralis*). Typically this snail is a clear yellow ground-colour with five sharp-edged brown to black spiral bands. But the snail is very variable and the ground colour can also be one of many shades of white, pink, reddish or brown. In addition, any one of the five bands may be absent, present and separate, or present and joined to the adjacent one. But the mouth of the shell usually has a brown-red lip which distinguishes it from the similarly variable white-lipped or garden snail (*Cepaea hortensis*).

The grove snail is an excellent subject for investigation, although the other species are equally good. Grove snails are often found in

Fig. 23 (a) Grey field slug (*Agriolimax reticulatus*) (b) large black slug (*Arion ater*) (c) grove snail (*Cepaea nemoralis*) (d) white-lipped or garden snail (*Cepaea hortensis*)

colonies at the bottom of the hedgerow, and an interesting experiment is to record carefully where you found a colony. Count how many snails are present and, with as little disturbance as possible, put a dab of quick-drying enamel paint on their shells. You should then return the following day and see whether the snails have moved off in search of food. Later visits to the site will tell you whether the snails have returned 'home' to the same spot, and if they do you will have some indication of their habits and life-span.

You might then go on to collect further quantities of the grove snails and make careful records as to the habitats in which they were found, such as grass verge, nettle bed, hawthorn hedge bottom, and note the colour of the individuals found in each site. Is any particular colour variety restricted to one particular habitat?

If there are any large stones in the vicinity which are used by thrushes as 'anvils' on which to crack open snail shells, you might examine the broken shells to see whether any particular colour of grove snail is more prone to predation in any particular area.

7·The Future of Hedgerows

The value of hedgerows to wild life

The many different types of foods and nesting sites that hedgerows provide for insects, birds, mammals and other animals, make them a valuable resource for the wild life of this country. It has been estimated that 10 million birds nest in hedgerows every year, and the hedges have helped to take over the role once provided by the fast-disappearing deciduous woodlands.

In addition, hedgerows may well provide important lines of communication for wild life, particularly as the remaining woodlands and other wild areas are becoming more and more fragmented. Were it not for the hedgerows that connect these habitats like highways, many cover-loving birds and mammals, like wrens and bank voles, would live in isolated woodlands. If the woods were cleared, then these birds and mammals might have nowhere to go.

The widespread removal of hedges in the last twenty-five years has, therefore, become a serious problem for the conservation of wild life in this country, particularly since the destruction and removal of our remaining deciduous woodland is continuing.

Threats to hedgerows

As we have seen, one of the reasons for the removal of hedges from many farms is that the maintenance of hedges is expensive in terms of time and money. Many were allowed to become neglected and overgrown, took up too much valuable land and were uprooted.

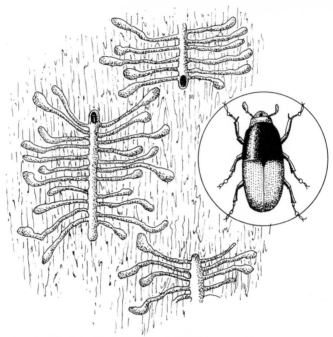

Fig. 24 Elm bark beetle (*Scolytus sp.*) and its burrow system

Others were removed by farmers because one large arable field was easier to cultivate and harvest with large modern machines than several small ones.

Since 1970 some hedges have been under a new threat. These are the hedges either containing elm trees or composed almost entirely of that species. Elm's most notorious insects are the elm bark beetles of the genus *Scolytus*. These beetles are small—about 6 mm long—and reddish-brown in colour. They live on the sugars and starches which they find as they burrow into the tree. Unfortunately, the beetles also carry a fungus called *Ceratocystis ulmi* which causes the very serious Dutch elm disease (so called because it almost wiped out the elms of Holland). In recent years, this disease has destroyed countless millions of elms in Britain.

And, as we have already seen, when a hedgerow is removed or destroyed, thousands of animals and plants lose their home, for good, and many die if there is not convenient woodland or hedgerow for them nearby in which they can seek sanctuary.

Since the removal of the Ministry of Agriculture subsidy, the rate of hedgerow removal has decreased, but the 960,000 km (600,000 miles) or so of hedgerow that we have left are by no means safe.

As well as the continuing threat from Dutch elm disease, many hedges have suffered from over-cutting by the modern tractor-drawn hedge-cutting machines. The chief disadvantage of these machines, which are quick and relatively cheap to operate, is that they cannot deal with the coarse vegetation at the bottom of a hedge. Nor can they select out, and leave, the strong young saplings which might grow into trees. Where the coarse vegetation at the bottom of the hedge is not brushed out regularly, it suppresses the more interesting plants and may eventually lead to the death of the hedge itself. On the other hand, where the hedge bottoms are cleaned out, the soil is disturbed and light is let in, and annual and biennial plants, as well as perennials, can become established. This leads in turn to a larger and more varied animal life.

Some other hedges have been accidentally or deliberately sprayed with insecticides and weedkiller, while even more have been destroyed where fires, intended to burn the stubble and surplus straw after corn harvesting, have got out of control. Thousands of hedges, particularly those near roads, lay-bys, picnic places or around areas of interest, have been heavily polluted by litter, deposited by selfish and thoughtless passers-by.

As well as being unsightly, much of this litter is dangerous to both farm animals and wild life. Animal protection organisations and veterinary surgeons, as well as farmers, see many cases of animal injury and death caused by litter. Jagged tins and broken glass are obviously dangerous; cattle and deer have been known to choke to death from eating polythene bags, and hedgehogs have caught their heads in yoghurt or cream cartons.

Milk bottles have been described as 'the glass coffins of the hedgerow', and the Milk Marketing Board loses more than half a million bottles a year, many of which undoubtedly end up in countryside hedgerows. Some small mammals seem unable to resist entering a small opening like the top of a milk bottle to explore. Once inside, they are unable to leave again because their tiny claws cannot grip the smooth, shiny surface of the upward-sloping neck of the bottle—even when it is lying on its side. Other animals may enter the bottle later, until it eventually becomes full, and the corpses attract carrion beetles which come and feed on the decaying flesh. These also become trapped and die, many being drowned by the rain water that gradually collects inside the bottle.

One milk bottle from a lay-by in Surrey contained twenty-seven dead mice, voles and shrews, indicating the effectiveness of these death-traps.

Discarded bottles are just one more of the hazards that hedgerow animals have to live with, and as well as the other threats we have already mentioned, there is the ever-present danger to wildlife in roadside hedgerows from motor vehicles.

Advantages and disadvantages to the farmer of hedgerow wild life

The advantages to the farmer of the wildlife in the hedgerows are not as clear-cut as was once supposed. Inevitably a hedge will contain animals harmful to crops such as aphids, winter moths, rabbits and wood pigeons, as well as those species which are neutral or positively beneficial. The dangers to crops are greater now with modern methods of farming than they were in the past, when fields were small and the crops grown were varied.

Where there is still a relatively large ratio of hedge to field, hedge-dwelling animals and plants exist in a highly complex association with one another and are normally in balance with man's activities around them.

Sometimes, however, particularly where vast areas are devoted to one crop and that same crop is grown year after year, the natural balance is upset. The pests of that particular crop may increase rapidly on the abundance of food available and outnumber their natural enemies. They then overwinter in the hedgerows and continue their attacks on the next year's crop. This has happened, for instance, with a number of aphid species in hedges near to where root crops and horticultural produce are being grown, and with bullfinches in fruit-growing districts. A number of crop diseases, particularly the mildews and rusts, also spend part of their life-cycle growing on hedgerow plants, whilst some hedgerow plants, notably nettles, thistles and couch grass, may find field conditions suitable for their growth and become weeds. Normally, however, the spread of seeds or plant parts from the hedges to the crops is insignificant compared with the 'seed bank' of weed species already present in the soil of fields.

Again, in the days when fields were small, and crops were varied and rotated, these explosions of pests and weeds would not have happened so easily, and there would have been a greater chance of a natural balance developing between the pest or weed and its enemies. Now there are many reasons why it is becoming increasingly necessary to spray crops against insect and weed pests. One reason is that the area devoted to a single crop has become so large that the predator species, the enemies of the insect pests, and the birds which eat weeds, cannot keep them under control. Many of these enemies of pests and weeds, particularly hedgehogs, spiders, ladybirds, and goldfinches and their relatives, live in hedges and similar places and range around for their food. If the hedges where they live disappear,

23. A shelter belt of pine trees (*Pinus sylvestris*) in the Breckland of East Anglia

so too will these beneficial animals, no matter how much food there is available to them.

One advantage of hedges is that researchers have shown that they can slow wind speeds significantly for up to 100 metres from the hedge. This decreases soil erosion, and protects the crops, thus giving better yields, while on livestock farms hedges can provide shade and shelter for domestic animals.

A major worry about hedgerow removal is not so much the national rate as the variation from place to place. The sad fact is that three-quarters of the hedges removed in any one year are from eastern England, where even in 1946 there were in some counties only 16 km (10 miles) or so of hedge for every square mile of farmland. By contrast the rate of hedgerow removal from the west of England is very low, and even now Devon, with its small fields, has about 40 km (25 miles) of hedge for every square mile of farmland.

In parts of Cambridgeshire, south Lincolnshire, Norfolk and Suffolk, the effects of no hedgerows over vast areas can be seen. The result is not only a very barren landscape, but also dust storms, caused by the wind eroding the fine topsoil. These 'prairie farms' would still seem to be increasing in a number of areas of intensive arable farming. If the present policy of hedge-removal continues, no doubt we shall have more and more examples of the kind of story which is told about a man whose farm was near the Norfolk–Suffolk border. When asked by a stranger in just which county his land was situated, the farmer's terse reply was: 'It all depends on which way the wind is blowing!'

Apart from this problem of wind-blown topsoil, to which the hedge is a real solution, and also the provision of shelter and shade, the advantage of a hedge to the farmer is that it acts as a barrier to livestock (and humans). But this function can equally well be carried out by barbed wire or electric fences. The latter are also less likely to harbour pests or to act as a dumping ground for litter discarded by the passing motorist. Wire fences are cheaper to maintain than hedges, even when modern hedge-cutting machines are used, they take up much less space, and they have the added advantage that they can be easily moved when necessary.

Hedgerow nature reserves

The most interesting hedge of all is the tall old hedge with a number of different shrub species in it. Such a hedge is of interest not only to naturalists but also to historians, for many such hedges mark the boundaries of parishes. Because of the history of land ownership in this country, these hedges are likely to mark the boundaries of farms as well. From the farmer's point of view, these hedges which divide his land off from his neighbour's are likely to be less of a nuisance than those hedges within his farm which were laid out for horse-drawn implements rather than the large machines of today.

Many of these parish boundary hedges have been there for over a thousand years. They are probably the most common relic of Saxon land settlement and use and, as such, are of great interest to the historian. Because they have existed for so long, these hedges have accumulated a larger number of species of plants than newer hedges, and the older they are the more they resemble our fast-disappearing deciduous woodland. As they have a diverse flora, these hedges are also better for birds, mammals, insects and other animal life. Hence, although ideally naturalists would like to conserve all hedges, these ancient boundary hedges are the ones to which they should give the greatest attention when hedges are threatened.

It is here that we come to the real problem. In a world where millions go to bed hungry every night, and in a country which has to import much of its food, which matters more, hedgerows or the valuable space they often take up? If we decide to keep hedges because they look attractive and we like the familiar chequered appearance they produce on the landscape, then who is to pay for their upkeep? Can we really expect the farmer to provide valuable and scarce time, machinery and manpower to clip, clean and lay hedges solely for the benefit of tourists, town-dwellers and naturalists? If not, who is to bear the cost?

The British Trust for Conservation Volunteers and many county naturalists' trusts are already doing valuable work in providing opportunities for young people to help conserve our diminishing natural environment, including the provision of training in hedge-laying by the traditional methods. Perhaps if our most interesting hedges are to be saved, then they will have to be treated like nature reserves, and the farmer on whose land they are situated will have to receive a grant for allowing them to remain, and assistance from young volunteers in seeing that they are properly cared for.

There is also plenty of space still left in the British Isles where hedgerow habitats could be created, in addition to the odd corners of farms where large machines do not have room to manoeuvre efficiently. Parks and the larger gardens could provide more cover than they do, and our many new and improved roads would be less drab and monotonous if they were enlivened by hedgerows. Again, the effort to ensure that new hedges are planted will probably have to come from keen and enlightened volunteers.

8·Studying a Hedgerow

Having read about some of the plants and animals to be found in hedgerows and the way in which their lives interact, you may like to carry out some investigations into your local hedgerows. Almost any kind of hedge will do; even a privet hedge in a garden or park can reveal a lot of interesting information. But the most fascinating hedge of all to study is one which contains a variety of shrub and tree species, especially if it is bounded by a ditch or grass verge. However, do remember that if the hedge is on private land, then you must seek permission first from the owner before you begin work.

1. A general survey of a hedge

As a preliminary investigation, you might try to answer the following questions about your selected hedge:

Where is your hedge and how long is it?

What is its average height?

Is it a parish boundary hedge or merely a boundary between two fields or a field and a road?

Is the hedge managed by clipping or laying, or is it unmanaged?

What large trees are present in the hedgerow?

Does the hedge consist of several kinds of shrub? If so, what species are present?

What other kinds of plant are present?

How are the groups of plants such as climbers, shade plants and scramblers, distributed?

Are the plants growing under hedgerow trees which cast shade different from those in the rest of the hedge?

How old do you estimate your hedge to be (see page 34)?

Are the populations of plants and animals on both sides of the hedge the same?

What kind of soil is the hedge growing on?

If the hedge has a ditch on one side, how do the plant species on the two sides compare?

If you can compare your hedge with others of different ages and in different parts of the country, different altitudes, under different types of management and on different types of soil, you can gain much interesting information. Or, more simply, are the populations of plants and animals in a hedge running from north to south the same as those in a similar hedge running from east to west?

2. A hedgerow bird census

List all the bird species seen in your hedge every week or every month for a whole year. This will reveal the species that are resident and those that are summer or winter visitors to the hedge. Use reference books to help you find out where the migrant species travel to or have come from. You might also compare the bird species that are present in the hedge at different times of the day during each of the four seasons.

How many birds are present in your hedge at different times of the year? You could take regular counts, preferably weekly, of the numbers of each species that you see along the hedge. Alternatively, you could concentrate on the numbers of a few selected species such as blackbirds, chaffinches or dunnocks. The counting is best done in the early morning when most birds are active and many are singing. Quietness is essential if you are not to drive all the birds away. After several counts you should be able to assess your results and obtain a fair estimate of the numbers of each species within your chosen length of hedge. The results can then be compared with those for other seasons of the year. If you can carry out censuses on two or more stretches of hedge of the same length, you can see what effect different shrub species and different types of hedgerow management have on the numbers and species of birds. In other words, you could find out which type of hedges are best for finding different species of birds.

3. Birds' nests

A very instructive study can be made of birds' nests. Some preliminary work can be done in the spring and summer, recording the position of any nests that you find and identifying the species to which they belong. Of course, it is vital not to disturb the birds or to touch the nest at this stage, or the birds may well desert it. Nor should you leave any evidence such as trampled vegetation that might give away the position of the nests to vandals, egg-thieves or other predators. Your detailed study can begin in the autumn after the young birds have flown and the nest has been deserted.

Before you remove each nest, record its exact position, including, if it is in a tree or shrub, the species of the plant and the height of the nest above the ground. When you have removed the nest, dust it with derris powder or one of the insect powders containing pyrethrum, to kill any parasites that may be lurking there, and then allow it to dry out thoroughly. Weigh the dried nest as accurately as you can, and then carefully pull it to pieces. Separate the material into heaps— mosses and lichens in one pile, dried grass in another, mud in another, twigs in another, and so on. Weigh or measure the contents of each pile.

Repeat this for as many nests as you can, and then draw up a list of the favourite nesting materials and preferred nest sites for each of the species you have studied.

4. Roosting birds

Most bird species appear to seek some shelter from wind and rain when roosting. Some species, notably starlings, rooks, crows, jackdaws, gulls, many finches, blackbirds and thrushes, use large communal roosts in autumn and winter. Sometimes several species roost together, whereas other flocks of roosting birds may be all of the same species.

Having found a communal roost in a hedge, measure the area covered and get there early to try to estimate the size of the flock. Keep records of the times of arrival of the birds and see how their arrival times are influenced by the length of day and weather conditions. Where do the birds go in the daytime? Do they remain in quite large flocks or do they break up into small groups to feed?

When you turn to those species which roost singly or in small groups, you will have quietly to search likely spots along the hedgerow with a dimmed torch. Remember, however, that a bird forced to leave its nest at night is in danger of being caught by an owl or of injuring itself as it flies in the dark. Another danger is that the bird may be forced to sleep in some exposed place; this could mean death to an underfed small bird in winter. It is, therefore, much kinder to look for roosting birds just before dawn when, if disturbed, they will have only a little time to wait until daylight.

Find out all you can about the sites each species uses for roosting: whether the bird usually roosts alone or in company, what time it goes to roost under a variety of weather conditions, and if its roosting times change throughout the year.

5. Birds and berries

During the autumn and winter, keep a watch on those trees and shrubs that have berries and other fruits, to see which species of birds eat the fruits and which kinds they prefer. Record your observations in the form of a table listing the date, place, number and species of the birds, and the types of fruits they were eating. A brief note on the weather conditions when each record was made would also be useful. Remember that you should take down details of only those birds actually *seen eating* the fruits, and not those that were just sitting in the tree or bush where the fruits were.

6. The vertical zonation of invertebrate animals in a hedgerow

The plants in a hedge grow to different heights and this results in four layers:

1. Tree layer—isolated trees such as oak, ash and elm.
2. Shrub layer—the main part of the hedge, including hawthorn, hazel and maple bushes.
3. Field layer—the herbaceous plants such as nettles, hogweed and grasses.
4. Litter layer—the dead leaves and mosses.

This division of the plants affects the vertical zonation of the animals, some of which live in all four layers, while others are restricted to a single layer. Begin by spreading out a white cotton or plastic sheet under a hedgerow tree. Shake the tree, or sharply tap its branches with a long stick. Then record the numbers of each animal species which fall into the sheet. Repeat this under several more trees, comparing different tree species if possible. The same technique is used for the hedgerow shrubs. Find out which species are living in the field layer by sweeping the vegetation with a net (page 100), and recording the numbers and species of animals as above. Repeat this as many times as possible. To extract larger invertebrates, shake the leaf litter in a garden sieve held over a sheet of white paper. Separate out the smaller animals from the litter by using one or other of the two pieces of apparatus shown in Fig. 25.

Record the species and their numbers from each layer as a block graph (histogram).

7. Pitfall traps

Some indication of the animal species present on the floor of the hedge can be obtained by using a pitfall trap. If the populations of small mammals are to be sampled, then a really large container such as a sweet jar or a large, deep tin should be sunk into the ground at the base of the hedge. If only the invertebrates are to be sampled, then smaller jars or tins are suitable. In either case the trap should be provided with a cover to prevent rainwater entering and drowning the catch (Fig. 26), but in any event it is only safe to use these traps during dry weather.

In the case of the large traps, it is a good idea to put a small handful of hay and a few oats in the traps or, if it is hoped to catch shrews, a

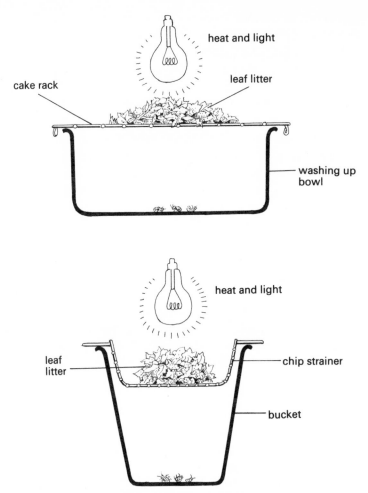

Fig. 25 Collecting the invertebrate animals from leaf litter

small piece of raw meat, tinned dog food or an earthworm. It is important that the traps should be inspected frequently—every two hours during the daytime is ideal, and if the traps are set last thing at night they should always be visited first thing next morning. When the catch has been examined, identified and recorded, it should be released near where it was caught.

Fig. 26 A pitfall trap

As well as lists of the animals present, you might for example, if you have several of the smaller traps, record the number of invertebrates such as woodlice, millipedes, centipedes or ground beetles caught during each month of the year. You could also compare the animal populations of different hedgerows.

It is most important that, if the traps are finished with, or you cannot visit them frequently, they are either removed completely or fitted with a tight-fitting lid, to prevent unnecessary suffering or loss of wild life.

8. Road-accident victims

Another way in which information can be obtained about the species of animals living in a hedge or using it as a temporary shelter is to study the road-accident victims near to it. This project is somewhat sad but, if you feel able to carry it out, it may help us to learn more about the causes of these accidents and, therefore, enable us to do something to prevent them.

Any length of road near to a hedge will do, and the ideal is one that you travel along regularly, perhaps on your way to school each day.

Every day record the number and species of animals that you find dead along your stretch of road and, if you have a map of the road, mark on it where each accident-victim was found. Where you can, pay particular attention as to whether the dead animal was an adult or a juvenile.

In which month or months are most animals killed? Which species are the most common victims? Are there any features, such as a gap in the hedge, a pond or a ditch, or a tall tree that might affect the number of animals killed during the night and early morning (count on your way to school), compared with the number killed during the rest of the day (count again in the evening on your way home)?

If possible, compare the results near different types of hedge and for different widths of road and grass verge. Perhaps you could exchange results with a friend in another part of the country.

Once an animal has been killed, what happens to its body? Keep watch on the corpse of a large and conspicuous mammal or bird from a safe distance, using binoculars if possible. Record any species of mammals, bird or other animal that you may see feeding on the corpse. If needs be, remove the corpse, using the blade of a trowel or spade, to a convenient, traffic-free place to watch it. If you are able to, you might repeat this observation at night, using a torch covered with a piece of red cellophane.

If a suitable hedge is available, lay the corpse of the road-accident victim, using a spade or a trowel, on to the surface of the soil at the foot of a hedge. Protect the corpse from cats and other larger animals by covering it with a garden cloche or a tent of wire netting.

How long does the corpse take to disappear? Try to identify the various kinds of insects, mainly beetles and the maggots of two-winged flies, responsible for the removal of the corpse. Samples of the maggots living in the corpse can be removed from time to time, using forceps, and kept in tins or jars of soil covered with a piece of old stocking until they pupate. Eventually the flies will hatch out and can then be identified.

9. Dangerous bottles

If you collect up empty bottles from the hedgerows, not only will you be helping to reduce the litter menace but you can, if you wish, also investigate the animal victims of the bottles. However, since the contents of the bottles may present a health hazard and have a powerful smell, it is important to take precautions, including wearing rubber gloves if these are available.

Empty the contents of each bottle into a clean screw-top jar, and add a little disinfectant immediately. Put on the lid and, when you get home, pour a little water into the container and a few drops of household bleach. Leave for twenty-four hours. Then rinse away as much of the fur and sludge as possible under the tap, tip out the solids remaining and put them on a separate piece of paper for further cleaning and identification. You might try collecting bottles from different kinds of hedgerows, for example from a hedge next to a ditch with water, near to a wood and an open field, to see whether there are any differences in the distribution of the mammals species. It is a good idea to make an exhibition of your findings to show your friends. This will discourage them from being careless with any bottles they have finished with.

10. Growing the seeds of hedgerow trees and shrubs

Tree and shrub seeds are best sown on collection between September and November, although there is a risk that they will be eaten during the winter by wood mice. Alternatively the seeds can be stored over the winter in tins or polythene bags of moist sand. In the case of some species, including holly, ash, elm and hawthorn, seeds must be stored in wet sand for about eighteen months. Inspect the seeds periodically in the spring for signs of growth, and sow them immediately they do begin to germinate.

The seeds can be sown in good garden soil or in boxes or pots of soil or seed compost. Plant the seeds about 5 cm deep, with at least 15 cm between each seed. The seedlings can be planted out in open ground in a frost-free period during the following winter and kept free from weeds. When they are about 25 to 60 cm high, they may be planted out in their permanent positions, which could be a gap in a hedgerow or a clearing in a wood if you can obtain permission. Alternatively you might find room for the young trees in the school grounds if there is not room for them in your own garden.

11. Grass verges

Grass verges are well worth studying because, as was mentioned on page 38, they often represent all that remains of the natural and semi-natural grasslands that were once plentiful.

You might begin by listing the plants which are present along a chosen strip of grass verge. It is helpful to know how common each plant is. If there is a lot of one species and it dominates the whole area, this plant is said to be *dominant*. A plant species is *abundant* if there is a lot of it about. If only one or two plants are found, the species is *rare*. When a few specimens are present the plant species is *occasional*, and if the plant is fairly common but not abundant, it is said to be *frequent*. The scale, in decreasing order of abundance is, therefore:

Dominant—Abundant—Frequent—Occasional—Rare

Many roadside verges are cut to improve visibility for drivers. Often only a metre or two of the verge nearest to the road is cut, leaving the rest untouched. How does the plant life of cut and uncut verges compare?

What effect does it have on the plant life if trenches or holes are dug into the grass verge to bury pipes, cables etc.?

If cars park on the verges, what effects do they have on the vegetation?

What are the effects of dumped rubbish or the heaps of grit and salt that are left for use during icy weather conditions?

Unfortunately, weedkillers are still occasionally used on grass verges. How do they affect the subsequent growth of plants?

Use pitfall traps (page 117) and sweep nets (page 100) to investigate the animal life of the verges and the effects of the various factors mentioned above on it.

12. The history of a hedgerow

It is not easy to find out details of the history of a really ancient hedgerow. The earliest reference to such a hedge is likely to be a boundary clause in an Anglo-Saxon Charter, and these are available for only a few parishes and are very difficult to interpret.

Details of the history of land used between 1066 and the middle of the sixteenth century are often also difficult to find. The most useful summary is likely to be in the appropriate volume of the *Victoria County History*. A set of these books should be available at the County Records Office, library or local museum.

From the end of the sixteenth century, the use of maps became more common and many County Record Offices have excellent collections of old estate maps. Most parishes were mapped at the time of enclosure and these maps may also be found at the Records Office or the parish church. Early Ordnance Survey maps of the area under study are extremely useful, as the $2\frac{1}{2}$-inch and 6-inch maps show field boundaries. Again the County Records Office will have a series of these, dating from the time of the first edition in 1884.

9·Further Reading and Information

(a) Books for identification

This first section lists some of the reference books available for identifying the plants and animals which can be found in hedgerows.

PLANT LIFE

Blamey, M., Fitter, R. and Fitter, A., *The Wild Flowers of Britain and Northern Europe*, Collins, London, 1974.

Brightman, F. H. and Nicholson, B. E., *The Oxford Book of Flowerless Plants*, O.U.P., London, 1966.

Keble-Martin, W., *The Concise British Flora in Colour*, Ebury Press, London, 1965.

McClintock, D. and Fitter, R. S. R., *Collins Pocket Guide to Wild Flowers*, Collins, London, 1965.

Mitchell, A., *A Field Guide to the Trees of Britain and Europe*, Collins, London, 1974.

Nicholson, B. E., Ary, S. and Gregory, M., *The Oxford Book of Wild Flowers*, O.U.P., London, 1960.

Stokoe, W. J., *Trees* (Observer Series), Warne, London, 1966.

Vedel, H. and Lange, J., *Trees and Bushes*, Methuen, London, 1960.

VERTEBRATES

Benson, S. Vere, *Birds* (Observer Series), Warne, London, 1952.

Burton, M., *Wild Animals of the British Isles* (Observer Series), Warne, London, 1960.

Fitter, R. S. R., and Richardson, R. A., *Collins Pocket Guide to British Birds*, Collins, London, 1966.

Holland, J., *Bird Spotting*, Blandford, London, 1963.

Jennings, T., *Mammals in Britain*, A. and C. Black, London, 1977.

Lawrence, J. and Brown, R. W., *Mammals of Britain, Their Tracks, Trails and Signs*, Blandford, London, 1973.

Nixon, M. and Whiteley, D., *The Oxford Book of Vertebrates*, O.U.P., London, 1972.

Corbet, G. B. and Southern, H. N., *The Handbook of British Mammals*, Blackwell, Oxford, Second Edition, 1977.

INVERTEBRATES

Burton, J., *The Oxford Book of Insects*, O.U.P., London, 1968.

Chinery, M., *A Field Guide to the Insects of Britain and Northern Europe*, Collins, London, 1973.

Lyneborg, L., *Moths in Colour*, Blandford, London, 1976.

Lyneborg, L., *Butterflies in Colour*, Blandford, London, 1975.

Lyneborg, L., *Field and Meadow Life in Colour*, Blandford, London, 1968.

Mandahl-Barth, G., *Woodland Life in Colour*, Blandford, London, 1966.

Nichols, D., Cooke, J. and Whiteley, D., *The Oxford Book of Invertebrates*, O.U.P., London, 1971.

(b) Books for general reading

These include books for readers who want to discover in more detail some aspects of hedgerows which have interested them in this book.

Automobile Association, *Book of the British Countryside*, Drive Publications, London, 1973.

Darlington, A., *The World of a Tree*, Faber and Faber, London, 1972.

Devon Trust for Nature Conservation, *School Projects in Natural History*, Heinemann, London, 1972.

Hoskins, W. G., *Fieldwork in Local History*, Faber and Faber, London, 1967.

Hoskins, W. G., *The Making of the English Landscape*, Penguin Books, London, 1970.

Jennings, T., *Studying Birds in the Garden*, Wheaton, Exeter, 1975.

Pollard, E., Hooper, M. D., and Moore, N. W., *Hedges*, Collins, London, 1974.

Simmons, G. E., *Plant and Animal Habitats in Town and Country*, Blandford, London, 1976.

(c) Useful addresses

Botanical Society of the British Isles
 c/o Department of Botany,
 British Museum (Natural History),
 Cromwell Road,
 London SW7

British Entomological and Natural History Society,
 23 Manor Way,
 North Harrow,
 Middlesex.

British Herpetological Society,
 c/o Zoological Society of London,
 Regents Park,
 London NW1 4RY

British Trust for Conservation Volunteers,
 Zoological Gardens,
 Regents Park,
 London NW1 4RY

Mammal Society of the British Isles,
 Harvest House,
 62 London Road, Reading, Berkshire.

Royal Society for the Protection of Birds,
  The Lodge,
  Sandy,
  Bedfordshire SG19 2DL
(Has a junior branch, the Young Ornithologists' Club).

Society for the Promotion of Nature Conservation,
  The Green,
  Nettleham.
  Lincoln LN2 2NR.
(Co-ordinates and provides information on the County Naturalists' Trusts)

Index